D0885386

TI-82
GRAPHING CALCULATOR
GUIDEBOOK

Guidebook developed by:
Texas Instruments Instructional Communications

With contributions by:

Richard G. Brown
Franklin Demana
Doug Feltz
Linda Ferrio
Greg Foley
Pat Hatcher
Michael Keyton
Pat Milheron
Jerry Murdock
Ann Phipps
Dave Santucci
John Stutzman
J. T. Sutcliffe
Chuck Vonder Embse
Bert K. Waits
C. B. Wilson
Lee E. Yunker

Richard G. Brown's
Precalculus class at
Phillips Exeter Academy:
Chris Alexander
Juhi Asad
Angelique Cooper
Keith Getchell
Elizabeth Gray
Suwha Hong
Toby Kiers
Emily B. Law
April Leightty
Kathryn Mak
Heather Melanson
Jason Pareti
Mahalakshimi Sarju
Enrique Smith

Important

Texas Instruments makes no warranty, either expressed or implied, including but not limited to any implied warranties of merchantability and fitness for a particular purpose, regarding any programs or book materials and makes such materials available solely on an "as-is" basis.

In no event shall Texas Instruments be liable to anyone for special, collateral, incidental, or consequential damages in connection with or arising out of the purchase or use of these materials, and the sole and exclusive liability of Texas Instruments, regardless of the form of action, shall not exceed the purchase price of this equipment. Moreover, Texas Instruments shall not be liable for any claim of any kind whatsoever against the use of these materials by any other party.

FCC Information Concerning Radio Frequency Interference

This equipment has been tested and found to comply with the limits for a Class B digital device, pursuant to Part 15 of the FCC rules. These limits are designed to provide reasonable protection against harmful interference in a residential installation. This equipment generates, uses, and can radiate radio frequency energy and, if not installed and used in accordance with the instructions, may cause harmful interference with radio communications. However, there is no guarantee that interference will not occur in a particular installation.

If this equipment does cause harmful interference to radio or television reception, which can be determined by turning the equipment off and on, you can try to correct the interference by one or more of the following measures:

- Reorient or relocate the receiving antenna.
- Increase the separation between the equipment and receiver.
- Connect the equipment into an outlet on a circuit different from that to which the receiver is connected.
- Consult the dealer or an experienced radio/television technician for help.

Caution: Any changes or modifications to this equipment not expressly approved by Texas Instruments may void your authority to operate the equipment.

This digital apparatus does not exceed the Class B limits for radio noise emissions from digital apparatus set out in the Radio Interference Regulations of the Canadian Department of Communications.

Table of Contents

This manual describes how to use the TI-82 Graphing Calculator. Getting Started gives a quick overview of its features. The first chapter gives general instructions on operating the TI-82. Other chapters describe its interactive features. The applications in Chapter 14 show how to use these features together.

Table of Contents (Continued)

Table of Contents (Continued)

Using this Guidebook Effectively

The structure of the TI-82 guidebook and the design of its pages can help you find the information you need quickly. Consistent presentation techniques are used throughout to make the guidebook easy to use.

Structure of the Guidebook

The guidebook contains sections that teach you how to use the calculator.

- Getting Started is a fast-paced keystroke-by-keystroke introduction.

- Chapter 1 describes general operation and lays the foundation for Chapters 2 through 13, which describe specific functional areas of the TI-82. Each begins with a brief Getting Started introduction.

- Chapter 14 contains application examples that incorporate features from different functional areas of the calculator. These examples can help you see how different functional areas work together to accomplish meaningful tasks.

- Chapter 15 describes memory management and Chapter 16 describes the communications link.

Page-Design Conventions

When possible, units of information are presented on a single page or on two facing pages. Several page-design elements help you find information quickly.

- **Page headings**—The descriptive heading at the top of the page or two-page unit identifies the subject of the unit.

- **General text**—Just below the page heading, a short section of bold text provides general information about the subject covered in the unit.

- **Left-column subheadings**—Each subheading identifies a specific topic or task related to the page or unit subject.

- **Specific text**—The text to the right of a subheading presents detailed information about that specific topic or task. The information may be presented as paragraphs, numbered procedures, bulleted lists, or illustrations.

- **Page "footers"**—The bottom of each page shows the chapter name, chapter number, and page number.

**Information-
Mapping
Conventions**

Several conventions are used to present information concisely and in an easily referenced format.

- **Numbered procedures**—A procedure is a sequence of steps that performs a task. In this guidebook, each step is numbered in the order in which it is performed. No other text in the guidebook is numbered; therefore, when you see numbered text, you know you must perform the steps sequentially.

- **"Bulleted" lists**—If several items have equal importance, or if you may choose one of several alternative actions, this guidebook precedes each item with a "bullet" (•) to highlight it—like this list.

- **Tables and charts**—Sets of related information are presented in tables or charts for quick reference.

- **Keystroke Examples**—The Getting Started examples provide keystroke-by-keystroke instructions, as do examples identified with a ⌨.

Reference Aids

Several techniques have been used to help you look up specific information when you need it. These include:

- A chapter table of contents on the first page of each chapter, as well as the full table of contents at the front of the guidebook.

- A glossary at the end of this section, defining important terms used throughout the guidebook.

- An alphabetical table of functions and instructions in Appendix A, showing their correct formats, how to access them, and page references for more information.

- Information about system variables in Appendix A.

- A table of error messages in Appendix B, showing the messages and their meanings, with problem-handling information.

- An alphabetical index at the back of the guidebook, listing tasks and topics you may need to look up.

Glossary

This glossary provides definitions for important terms that are used throughout this guidebook.

Expression	An expression is a complete sequence of numbers, variables, functions, and their arguments that can be evaluated to a single answer.
Function	A function, which may have arguments, returns a value and can be used in an expression.
	A function is also the expression entered in the Y= editor used in graphing and TABLE.
Graph Database	A graph database is composed of the elements that define a graph: functions in the Y= list, MODE settings, and WINDOW settings. They may be saved as unit in a graph database to recreate the graph later.
Graph Picture	A picture is a saved image of a graph display, excluding cursor coordinates, axis labels, tick marks, and prompts. It may be superimposed on another graph.
Home Screen	The Home Screen is the primary screen of the TI-82, where expressions can be entered and evaluated and instructions can be entered and executed.
Instruction	An instruction, which may have arguments, initiates an action. Instructions are not valid in expressions.
List	A list is a set of values that the TI-82 can use for activities such as graphing a family of curves, evaluating a function at multiple values, and entering statistical data.
Matrix	A matrix is a two-dimensional array on which the TI-82 can perform operations.
Menu Items	Menu items are shown on full-screen menus.
Pixel	A pixel (picture element) is a square dot on the TI-82 display. The TI-82 display is 96 pixels wide and 64 pixels high.
Variable	A variable is the name given to a location in memory in which a value, an expression, a list, a matrix, or another named item is stored.

Getting Started: Do This First!

Getting Started contains two keystroke-by-keystroke examples, an interest rate problem and a volume problem, that introduce you to some principal operating and graphing features of the TI-82. You will learn to use the TI-82 much more quickly by completing both of these examples first.

TI-82 Menus

To leave the keyboard uncluttered, the TI-82 uses full-screen menus to access many additional operations. The use of specific menus is described in the appropriate chapters.

Displaying a Menu

When you press a key that accesses a menu, such as [MATH], that menu screen temporarily replaces the screen where you are working.

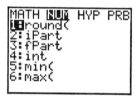

After you make a selection from a menu, you usually are returned to the screen where you were.

Moving from One Menu to Another

A menu key may access more than one menu. The names of the menus appear on the top line. The current menu is highlighted and the items in that menu are displayed.

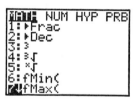

Use [▶] or [◀] to display a different menu.

Selecting an Item from a Menu

The number of the current item is highlighted. If there are more than seven items on the menu, a ↓ appears on the last line in place of the : (colon).

To select from a menu:
- Use [▼] and [▲] to move the cursor to the item and then press [ENTER].
- Press the number of the item.

Leaving without Making a Selection

To leave a menu without making a selection:
- Press [2nd] [QUIT] to return to the Home screen.
- Press [CLEAR] to return to the screen where you were.
- Select another screen or menu.

First Steps

Before beginning these sample problems, follow the steps on this page to reset the TI-82 to its factory settings. (Resetting the TI-82 erases all previously entered data.) This ensures that following the keystrokes in this section produces the illustrated actions.

1. Press [ON] to turn the calculator on.

2. Press and release [2nd] and then press [+].
   (Pressing [2nd] accesses the operation
   printed in blue to the left above the next
   key that you press. MEM is the
   2nd operation of [+].)

   The MEMORY menu is displayed.

3. Press **3** to select **Reset....**

   The RESET MEMORY menu is displayed.

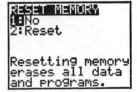

4. Press **2** to select **Reset**. The calculator is
   reset.

5. After a reset, the display contrast is also
   reset. If the screen is very dark or blank,
   you need to adjust the display contrast.
   Press [2nd] and then press and hold [▼] (to
   make the display lighter) or [▲] (to make
   the display darker). You can press
   [CLEAR] to clear the display.

Mem cleared

Entering a Calculation: Compound Interest

Using trial and error, determine when $1000 invested at 6% annual compounded interest will double in value. The TI-82 displays up to 8 lines of 16 characters so you see an expression and its solution at the same time. You also can store values to variables, enter multiple instructions on one line, and recall previous entries.

1. Press **.06** STO► ALPHA I (annual interest rate) to store the interest rate.

2. Press 2nd [:] to enter more than one instruction on a line.

3. For the first guess, compute the amount available at the end of 10 years. Enter **10** STO► ALPHA **Y** (years).

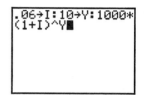

4. Press 2nd [:], then enter the expression to calculate the total amount available after **Y** years at I interest just as you would write it. Press **1000** × ⟦ **1** + ALPHA I ⟧ ^ ALPHA **Y**.

   The entire problem is shown in the first two lines of the display.

5. Press ENTER to evaluate the expression.

   The answer is shown on the right side of the display. The cursor is positioned on the next line, ready for you to enter the next expression.

6. To save keystrokes, you can use Last Entry to recall the last expression entered and then edit it for a new calculation. Press 2nd, followed by [ENTRY] (above ENTER).

   The last calculated expression is shown on the next line of the display.

7. The next guess should be greater than
    10 years. Make the next guess 12 years.
    Press △ to move the cursor over the **0**,
    and then type **2** to change **10** to **12**.
    Press [ENTER] to evaluate the expression.

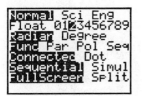

8. To display answers in a format more
    appropriate for calculations involving
    money, press [MODE] to display the MODE
    screen.

9. Press ▽ ▷ ▷ ▷ to position the cursor
    over the 2 and then press [ENTER]. This
    changes the display format to two fixed
    decimal places.

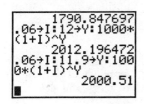

10. Press [2nd] [QUIT] (above [MODE]) to return
    to the Home screen. The next guess
    should be less than, but close to, 12
    years. Press [2nd] [ENTRY] △ **1** [2nd] [INS]
    (above [DEL]) **.9** to change 12 to 11.9.
    Press [ENTER] to evaluate the expression.

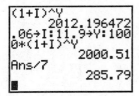

11. If the amount above is to be divided
    among seven people, how much will
    each person get? To divide the last
    calculated amount by seven, press ÷ **7**,
    followed by [ENTER].

    As soon as you press ÷, **Ans/** is
    displayed at the beginning of the new
    expression. **Ans** is a variable that
    contains the last calculated answer.

Defining a Function: Box with Lid

Take an 8½"×11" sheet of paper and cut X by X squares from two corners and X by 5½" rectangles from the other two corners. Now fold the paper into a box with lid. What X would give the maximum volume V of a box made in this way? Use tables and graphs to determine the solution.

Begin by defining a function that describes the volume of the box.

From the diagram:

$$2X + A = W$$
$$2X + 2B = L$$
$$V = A B X$$

Substituting: $V = (W - 2X)(L / 2 - X) X$

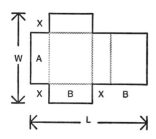

1. Press MODE ▼ ENTER to change the MODE back to **Float**.

2. Press 2nd [Quit] CLEAR to return to the Home screen and clear it.

3. Press **8.5** STO► ALPHA **W** 2nd [:] **11** STO► ALPHA **L** ENTER to store the width and length of the paper.

```
8.5→W:11→L
               11
■
```

4. You define functions for tables and graphing on the Y= edit screen. Press Y= to access this screen.

```
\Y1=■
\Y2=
\Y3=
\Y4=
\Y5=
\Y6=
\Y7=
\Y8=
```

5. Enter the function for volume as **Y1**. Press (ALPHA **W** − 2 X,T,Θ) ((ALPHA **L** ÷ 2 − X,T,Θ)) X,T,Θ ENTER to define function **Y1** in terms of **X**. (X,T,Θ lets you enter **X** quickly, without pressing ALPHA.)

The = sign is highlighted to show that **Y1** is selected.

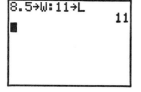

```
\Y1 ■(W-2X)(L/2-X)
X
\Y2=■
\Y3=
\Y4=
\Y5=
\Y6=
\Y7=
```

Defining a Table of Values

The table feature of the TI-82 provides numeric information about a function. Use a table of values from the previously defined function to estimate an answer to the problem.

1. Press [2nd] [TblSet] (above [WINDOW]) to display the TABLE SETUP menu.

2. Press [ENTER] to accept **TblMin=0**.

3. Press .5 [ENTER] to define the table increment ΔTbl=.5. Leave **Indpnt: Auto** and **Depend: Auto** so the table will be generated automatically.

4. Press [2nd] [TABLE] (above [GRAPH]) to display the table.

   Note that the maximum value is around **1.5**, between **1** and **2**.

5. Press and hold [▼] to scroll the table until the sign change appears. Note that the maximum length of **X** for this problem occurs where the sign of **Y₁** (volume) becomes negative.

6. Press [2nd] [TblSet]. Note that **TblMin** has changed to reflect the first line of the table you last displayed.

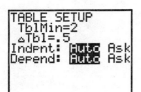

Zooming In on the Table

You can adjust the way a table is displayed to get more detailed information about any defined function. By varying the value of ΔTbl, you can "zoom in" on the table.

1. Adjust the table setup to get a more accurate estimate of the maximum size of the cutout. Press **1** [ENTER] to set **TblMin**. Press **.1** [ENTER] to set ΔTbl.

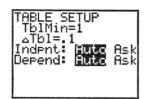

```
TABLE SETUP
 TblMin=1
 ΔTbl=.1
Indpnt: Auto Ask
Depend: Auto Ask
```

2. Press [2nd] [Table].

```
   X      Y₁
  1      29.25
  1.1    30.492
  1.2    31.476
  1.3    32.214
  1.4    32.718
  1.5    33
  1.6    33.072
 X=1
```

3. Use ⊟ and ⊡ to scroll the table. Note that the maximum value displayed is **33.072**, which occurs at **X**=1.6. The maximum occurs at 1.5<**X**<1.7.

```
   X      Y₁
  1.2    31.476
  1.3    32.214
  1.4    32.718
  1.5    33
  1.6    33.072
  1.7    32.946
  1.8    32.634
 X=1.8
```

4. Press [2nd] [TblSet]. Press **1.5** [ENTER] to set **TblMin**. Press **.01** [ENTER] to set △**Tbl**.

```
TABLE SETUP
 TblMin=1.5
 △Tbl=.01
Indpnt: Auto Ask
Depend: Auto Ask
```

5. Press [2nd] [Table] and use ▼ and ▲ to scroll the table. Two "equal" maximum values are shown, **33.074** at **X**=**1.58** and **X**=**1.59**.

```
  X  │ Y1  │
1.55 │33.062│
1.56 │33.068│
1.57 │33.072│
1.58 │33.074│
1.59 │33.074│
1.6  │33.072│
     │33.068│
X=1.61
```

6. Press ▼ and ▲ to move the cursor to **1.58**. Press ▶ to move the cursor into the **Y1** column. The bottom line of the display shows the value of **Y1** at **1.58** in full precision, **33.073824**.

```
  X  │ Y1  │
1.55 │33.062│
1.56 │33.068│
1.57 │33.072│
1.58 │33.074│
1.59 │33.074│
1.6  │33.072│
1.61 │33.068│
Y1=33.073824
```

7. Press ▼ to display the "other" maximum. The value of **Y1** at **1.59** in full precision is **33.073908**. This would be the maximum volume of the box if you could cut your piece of paper at .01 inch increments.

```
  X  │ Y1  │
1.55 │33.062│
1.56 │33.068│
1.57 │33.072│
1.58 │33.074│
1.59 │33.074│
1.6  │33.072│
1.61 │33.068│
Y1=33.073908
```

Changing the Viewing WINDOW

The viewing WINDOW defines the portion of the coordinate plane that appears in the display. The values of the WINDOW variables determine the size of the viewing WINDOW. You can view and change these values.

1. Press [WINDOW] to display the WINDOW variables edit screen. You can view and edit the values of the WINDOW variables here.

```
WINDOW FORMAT
Xmin=-10
Xmax=10
Xscl=1
Ymin=-10
Ymax=10
Yscl=1
```

The standard WINDOW variables define the viewing WINDOW as shown. **Xmin, Xmax, Ymin,** and **Ymax** define the boundaries of the display. **Xscl** and **Yscl** define the distance between tick marks on the **X** and **Y** axis.

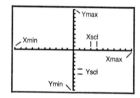

2. Press [▼] to move the cursor onto the line to define **Xmin**. Press 0 [ENTER].

3. You can enter expressions to define values in the WINDOW editor. Press **8.5** [÷] **2.**

```
WINDOW FORMAT
Xmin=0
Xmax=8.5/2█
Xscl=1
Ymin=-10
Ymax=10
Yscl=1
```

4. Press [ENTER]. The expression is evaluated and **4.25** is stored in **Xmax**. Press [ENTER] to accept **Xscl** as **1**.

5. Press 0 [ENTER] 40 [ENTER] 10 [ENTER] to define the **Y** WINDOW variables.

```
WINDOW FORMAT
Xmin=0
Xmax=4.25
Xscl=1
Ymin=0
Ymax=40
Yscl=10
```

Displaying and Tracing the Graph

Now that you have defined the function to be graphed and the WINDOW in which to graph it, you can display and explore the graph. You can trace along a function with TRACE.

---

1. Press GRAPH to graph the selected function in the viewing WINDOW.

   The graph of $Y_1=(W-2X)(L/2-X)X$ is shown in the display.

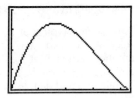

2. Press ▶ once to display the free-moving graph cursor just to the right of the center of the screen. The bottom line of the display shows the **X** and **Y** coordinate values for the position of the graph cursor.

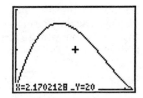

3. Use the cursor-keys (◀, ▶, ▲, and ▼) to position the free-moving cursor at the apparent maximum of the function.

   As you move the cursor, **X** and **Y** coordinate values are updated continually with the cursor position.

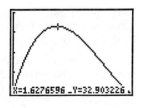

4. Press TRACE. The TRACE cursor appears on the Y_1 function near the middle of the screen. **1** in the upper right corner of the display shows that the cursor is on Y_1. As you press ◀ and ▶, you TRACE along Y_1, one **X** dot at a time, evaluating Y_1 at each **X**.

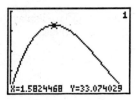

   Press ◀ and ▶ until you are on the maximum **Y** value. This is the maximum of $Y_1(X)$ for the **X** pixels. (There may be a maximum "in between" pixels.)

Zooming on the Graph

You can magnify the viewing WINDOW around a specific location using the ZOOM instructions to help identify maximums, minimums, roots, and intersections of functions.

1. Press ZOOM to display the ZOOM menu.

   This menu is typical of TI-82 menus. To select an item, you may either press the number to the left of the item, or you may press ▾ until the item number is highlighted and then press ENTER.

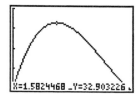

2. To zoom in, press **2**. The graph is displayed again. The cursor has changed to indicate that you are using a ZOOM instruction.

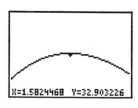

3. Use ◀, ▲, ▶, and ▾ to position the cursor near the maximum value on the function and press ENTER.

   The new viewing WINDOW is displayed. It has been adjusted in both the **X** and **Y** directions by factors of 4, the values for ZOOM factors.

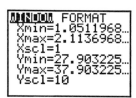

4. Press WINDOW to display the new WINDOW settings.

```
WINDOW FORMAT
Xmin=1.0511968...
Xmax=2.1136968...
Xscl=1
Ymin=27.903225...
Ymax=37.903225...
Yscl=10
```

Finding the Calculated Maximum

You can use a CALC operation to calculate a local maximum of a function.

1. Press [2nd] [CALC] to display the CALCULATE menu. Press **4** to select **maximum**.

   The graph is displayed again, with a prompt for Lower Bound?

   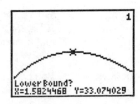

2. Use [◄] to trace along the curve to a point to the left of the maximum and then press [ENTER].

   A triangle at the top of the screen indicates the selected bound. A new prompt is displayed for Upper Bound?

   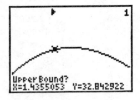

3. Use [►] to trace along the curve to a point to the right of the maximum and then press [ENTER].

   A triangle at the top of the screen indicates the selected bound. A new prompt is displayed for Guess?

   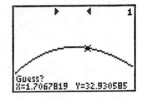

4. Use [◄] to trace to a point near the maximum and press [ENTER]. The answer is displayed at the bottom of the display.

   Note how the values for the calculated maximum compared with the maximums found with the free-moving cursor, TRACE, and the table.

   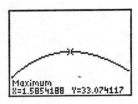

Other Features

Getting Started introduced you to basic calculator operation and the table and function graphing features of the TI-82. The remainder of this guidebook describes these features in more detail and also covers other capabilities of the TI-82.

Graphing	You can store, graph, and analyze up to ten functions (Chapter 3), up to six parametric functions (Chapter 4), and up to six polar functions (Chapter 5). You can use DRAW operations to annotate graphs (Chapter 8).
Sequences	You can generate sequences and graph them over time or as web plots. (Chapter 6)
Tables	You can create function evaluation tables to analyze multiple functions simultaneously. (Chapter 7)
Matrices	You can enter and save up to five matrices and perform standard matrix operations on them. (Chapter 10)
Lists	You can enter and save up to six lists for use in statistical analysis. You also can use lists to evaluate expressions at multiple values simultaneously and to graph a family of curves. (Chapter 11)
Statistics	You can perform one-variable and two-variable list-based statistical analysis, including median-median line and regression analysis, and plot the data as histograms, points, x-y lines, or box-and-whisker plots. You can define and save three statistical plot definitions. (Chapters 12).
Programming	You can enter and save programs that include extensive control and input/output instructions. (Chapter 13)
Split Screen	You can show simultaneously the graph screen and a related editor, such as the Y= screen, table, list editor, or Home screen. (Chapter 9)

Chapter 1: Operating the TI-82

This chapter describes the TI-82 and provides general information about its operation.

Turning the TI-82 On and Off

To turn the TI-82 on, press the [ON] key. To turn it off, press and release [2nd] and then press [OFF]. After about five minutes without any activity, APD™ (Automatic Power Down) turns the TI-82 off automatically.

Turning the Calculator On

Press [ON] to turn the TI-82 on.

- If you pressed [2nd] [OFF] to turn the calculator off, the display shows the Home screen as it was when you last used it, and errors are cleared.

- If APD turned the calculator off, the TI-82, including the display, cursor, and any error conditions, will be exactly as you left it.

Turning the Calculator Off

Press and release [2nd] and then press [OFF] to turn the TI-82 off.

- Any error condition is cleared.

- All settings and memory contents are retained by Constant Memory™.

APD™ (Automatic Power Down)

To prolong the life of the batteries, APD turns the TI-82 off automatically after several minutes without any activity. When you press [ON], the TI-82 will be exactly as you left it.

- The display, cursor, and any error conditions are exactly as you left them.

- All settings and memory contents are retained by Constant Memory.

Batteries

The TI-82 uses four AAA alkaline batteries and has a user-replaceable back-up lithium battery. To replace batteries without losing any information stored in memory, follow the directions on page B-2.

Setting the Display Contrast

The brightness and contrast of the display depends on room lighting, battery freshness, viewing angle, and adjustment of the display contrast. The contrast setting is retained in memory when the TI-82 is turned off.

Adjusting the Display Contrast

You can adjust the display contrast to suit your viewing angle and lighting conditions at any time. As you change the contrast setting, the display contrast changes, and a number in the upper right corner indicates the current contrast setting between 0 (lightest) and 9 (darkest).

Note that there are 32 different contrast levels, so each number 0 through 9 represents more than one setting.

To adjust the contrast:

1. Press and release the 2nd key.

2. Use one of two keys:

   • To increase the contrast, press and hold ▲.

   • To decrease the contrast, press and hold ▼.

Note: If you adjust the contrast setting to zero, the display may become completely blank. If this happens, press and release 2nd and then press and hold ▲ until the display reappears.

When to Replace Batteries

When the batteries are low, the display begins to dim (especially during calculations), and you must adjust the contrast to a higher setting. If you find it necessary to set the contrast to a setting of 8 or 9, you should replace the four AAA batteries soon.

Note: The display contrast may appear very dark after you change batteries. Press and release 2nd and then press and hold ▼ to lighten the display.

The Display

The TI-82 displays both text and graphics. Graphics are described in Chapter 3. The TI-82 also can display a split screen, showing graphics and text simultaneously (Chapter 9).

Home Screen

The Home screen is the primary screen of the TI-82, where you enter instructions to be executed and expressions to be evaluated and see the answers.

Displaying Entries and Answers

When text is displayed, the TI-82 screen can have up to eight lines of up to 16 characters per line. If all lines of the display are filled, text "scrolls" off the top of the display. If an expression on the Home screen, the Y= editor (Chapter 3), or the program editor (Chapter 13) is longer than one line, it wraps to the beginning of the next line. On numeric editors such as the WINDOW screen (Chapter 3), an expression scrolls to the left and right.

When an entry is executed on the Home screen, the answer is displayed on the right side of the next line.

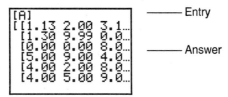

```
log 2
         .3010299957
```
——— Entry
——— Answer

The MODE settings control the way expressions are interpreted and answers are displayed (page 1-10).

If an answer, such as a list or matrix, is too long to display in its entirety, ellipsis marks (...) are shown at the left or right. Use ▷ and ◁ to scroll the answer and view all of it.

```
[A]
[[1.13 2.00 3.1...
 [1.30 9.99 0.0...
 [0.00 0.00 8.0...
 [5.00 9.00 4.0...
 [4.00 2.00 8.0...
 [4.00 5.00 9.0...
```
——— Entry

——— Answer

Returning to the Home Screen

To return to the Home screen from any other screen, press [2nd] [QUIT].

Display Cursors In most cases, the appearance of the cursor indicates what will happen when you press the next key.

Cursor	Appearance	Meaning
Entry	Solid blinking rectangle	The next keystroke is entered at the cursor; it types over any character.
INS (insert)	Blinking underline	The next keystroke is inserted in front of the cursor location.
2nd	Blinking ↑ (arrow)	The next keystroke is a 2nd operation.
ALPHA	Blinking A	The next keystroke is an alphabetic character.
"full"	Checkerboard rectangle	You have entered the maximum characters in a name, or memory is full.

If you press ALPHA or 2nd during an insertion, the underline cursor changes to an underlined A or ↑ cursor.

If you press 2nd or ALPHA on a screen on which there is no edit cursor (such as the MODE screen or a graph), ↑ or A appears in the upper right corner.

Graphs and the screens for viewing and editing tables, matrices, and lists have different cursors, which are described in the appropriate chapter.

Busy Indicator When the TI-82 is calculating or graphing, a moving vertical bar shows in the upper right of the display as a busy indicator. (When you pause a graph or a program, the busy indicator is a dotted bar.)

Entering Expressions and Instructions

On the TI-82, you can enter expressions, which return a value, in most places where a value is required. You enter instructions, which initiate an action, on the Home screen or in the program editor (Chapter 13).

Expressions

An expression is a complete sequence of numbers, variables, functions, and their arguments that evaluate to a single answer. On the TI-82, you enter an expression in the same order that it normally is written. For example, πR^2 is an expression.

Expressions can be used on the Home screen to calculate an answer. In most places where a value is required, expressions may be used to enter a value.

Entering an Expression

To create an expression, enter numbers, variables, and functions from the keyboard and menus. An expression is completed when you press ENTER, regardless of the cursor location. The entire expression is evaluated according to EOS rules (page 1-20), and the answer displayed.

Most TI-82 functions and operations are symbols with several characters in them. You must enter the symbol from the keyboard or menu, not spell it out. For example, to calculate the log of 45, you must press LOG 4 5. You cannot type in the letters L O G. (If you type LOG, the TI-82 interprets the entry as implied multiplication of the variables L, O, and G.)

Calculate $3.76 \div (\text{-}7.9 + \sqrt{5}) + 2 \log 45$.

3.76 ÷ (((-) 7.9 + 2nd [√] 5) + 2 LOG 45
ENTER

```
3.76/(-7.9+√5)+2
log 45
          2.642575252
```

Multiple Entries on a Line

To enter more than one expression or instruction on a line, separate them with a colon (:). They are all stored together in Last Entry (page 1-14).

```
5→A:2→B:A/B
          2.5
```

Entering a Number in Scientific Notation

1. Type the part of the number that precedes the exponent. This value can be an expression.

2. Press [2nd] [EE]. ε appears in the display.

3. If the exponent is negative, press [(-)] and then type the exponent, which can be one or two digits.

```
(19/2)ε⁻²
            .095
```

Entering a number in scientific notation does not cause the answers to be displayed in scientific or engineering notation. The display format is determined by the MODE settings (page 1-10) and the size of the number.

Functions

A function returns a value. For example, ÷, -, +, √, and **log** were the functions in the previous example. In general, the names of functions on the display begin with a lowercase letter. Some functions take more than one argument, which is indicated by a **(** at the end of the name. For example, **min(** requires arguments, **min(5,8)**.

Instructions

An instruction initiates an action. For example, **ClrDraw** is an instruction that clears any drawn elements from a graph. Instructions cannot be used in expressions. In general, the names of instructions begin with a capital letter. Some instructions require more than one argument, which is indicated by a **(** at the end of the name. For example, **Circle(** requires three arguments, **Circle(0,0,5)**.

Interrupting a Calculation

While the busy indicator is displayed, indicating that a calculation or a graph is in progress, you can press [ON] to stop the calculation. (There may be a delay.) Except in graphing, the ERR:BREAK screen is shown.

• To go to where the interruption occurred, select **Goto**.

• To return to the Home screen, select **Quit**.

TI-82 Edit Keys

The arrow keys in the upper right of the keyboard control the movement of the cursor. In normal entry, a keystroke types over the character or characters at the position of the cursor. The [DEL] and [2nd] [INS] keys delete or insert characters.

▶ or ◀	Moves the cursor within an expression. These keys repeat.
▲ or ▼	Moves the cursor between lines. These keys repeat.
	• On top line of an expression on the Home screen, ▲ moves the cursor to beginning of expression.
	• On bottom line of an expression on the Home screen, ▼ moves the cursor to end of expression.
[2nd] ◀	Moves the cursor to beginning of expression.
[2nd] ▶	Moves the cursor to end of expression.
[ENTER]	Evaluates an expression or executes an instruction.
[CLEAR]	• On a line with text on the Home screen, clears (blanks) the current line.
	• On a blank line on the Home screen, clears everything on the Home screen.
	• In an editor, clears (blanks) expression or value where cursor is located; it does not store a zero.
[DEL]	Deletes character at cursor. This key repeats.
[2nd] [INS]	Inserts characters at underline cursor. To end insertion, press [2nd] [INS] or a cursor-key.
[2nd]	Next keypress is a 2nd operation (the blue operation to the left above a key). The cursor changes to an ↑. To cancel 2nd, press [2nd].
[ALPHA]	Next keypress is an ALPHA character (the gray character to the right above the key). The cursor changes to an A. To cancel ALPHA, press [ALPHA] or a cursor-key.
[2nd] [A-LOCK]	Sets ALPHA-LOCK; each subsequent keypress is an ALPHA character. The cursor changes to an A. To cancel ALPHA-LOCK, press [ALPHA]. Note that prompts for names automatically set the keyboard in ALPHA-LOCK.
[X,T,Θ]	Allows you to enter an **X** in **Func** MODE, a **T** in **Par** MODE, or a θ in **Pol** MODE without pressing [ALPHA] first.

Setting Modes

Modes control how numbers and graphs are displayed and interpreted. MODE settings are retained by Constant Memory™ when the TI-82 is turned off. All numbers, including elements of matrices and lists, are displayed according to the current MODE settings.

Checking MODE Settings

Press [MODE] to display the MODE settings. The current settings are highlighted. The specific MODE settings are described on the following pages.

Normal Sci Eng	Numeric display format
Float 0123466789	Number of decimal places
Radian Degree	Unit of angle measure
Func Par Pol Seq	Type of graphing
Connected Dot	Whether to connect graph points
Sequential Simul	Whether to plot simultaneously
FullScreen Split	Full or split screen

Changing MODE Settings

1. Use ⊟ or ⊡ to move the cursor to the line of the setting that you want to change. The setting that the cursor is on blinks.

2. Use ⊡ or ⊡ to move the cursor to the setting that you want.

3. Press [ENTER].

Leaving the MODE Screen

To leave the MODE screen:

• Press the appropriate keys to go to another screen.

• Press [2nd] [QUIT] or [CLEAR] to return to the Home screen.

Setting a MODE from a Program

You can set a MODE from a program by entering the name of the MODE as an instruction; for example, **Func** or **Float**. From a blank line, select the name from the interactive MODE selection screen in the program editor (Chapter 13); the name is copied to the cursor location. The format for fixed decimal setting is **Fix** n.

TI-82 Modes

The TI-82 has seven MODE settings. Three are related to how numeric entries are interpreted or displayed and four are related to how graphs appear in the display. Modes are set on the MODE screen (page 1-9).

Normal
Sci ·
Eng

Notation formats affect only how an answer is displayed on the Home screen. Numeric answers can display with up to 10 digits and a two-digit exponent. You can enter a number in any format.

Normal display format is the way in which we usually express numbers, with digits to the left and right of the decimal, as in **12346.67**.

Sci (scientific) notation expresses numbers in two parts. The significant digits display with one digit to the left of the decimal. The appropriate power of 10 displays to the right of E, as in **1.234667E4**.

Eng (engineering) notation is similar to scientific notation. However, the number may have one, two, or three digits before the decimal, and the power-of-10 exponent is a multiple of three, as in **12.34667E3**.

Note: If you select normal display format, but the answer cannot display in 10 digits or the absolute value is less than .001, the TI-82 changes to scientific notation for that answer only.

Float
Fix

Decimal settings affect only how an answer is displayed on the Home screen. They apply to all three notation display formats. You can enter a number in any format.

Float (floating) decimal setting displays up to 10 digits, plus the sign and decimal.

The fixed decimal setting displays the selected number of digits (**0** to **9**) to the right of the decimal. Place the cursor on the number of decimal digits you want and press [ENTER].

Radian **Degree**	Angle settings control how the TI-82 interprets angle values in trig functions and polar/rectangular conversions.
	Radian interprets the values as radians. Answers display in radians.
	Degree interprets the values as degrees. Answers display in degrees.
Func **Par** **Pol** **Seq**	**Func** (function) graphing plots functions where **Y** is a function of **X** (Chapter 3).
	Par (parametric) graphing plots relations where **X** and **Y** are functions of **T** (Chapter 4).
	Pol (polar) graphing plots functions where **R** is a function of θ (Chapter 5).
	Seq (sequence) graphing plots sequences (Chapter 6).
Connected **Dot**	**Connected** draws a line between the points calculated for the selected functions.
	Dot plots only the calculated points of the selected functions.
Sequential **Simul**	**Sequential** graphing evaluates and plots one function completely before the next function is evaluated and plotted.
	Simul (simultaneous) graphing evaluates and plots all selected functions for a single value of **X** and then evaluates and plots them for the next value of **X**.
FullScreen **Split**	**FullScreen** uses the entire screen to display a graph or edit screen.
	Split screen displays the current graph on the upper portion of the screen and the Home screen or an editor on the lower portion (Chapter 9).

Variable Names

On the TI-82 you can enter and use several types of data, including real numbers, matrices, lists, functions, stat plots, graph databases, and graph pictures.

Variables and Defined Items

The TI-82 uses preassigned names for variables and other items saved in memory.

Variable type	Names
Real numbers	A, B, . . . , Z, θ
Matrices	[A], [B], [C], [D], [E]
Lists	L1, L2, L3, L4, L5, L6
Functions	Y1, Y2, . . . , Y9, Y0
Parametric equations	X1T/Y1T, . . . , X6T/Y6T
Polar functions	r1, r2, r3, r4, r5, r6
Sequence functions	Un, Vn
Stat plots	Plot1, Plot2, Plot3
Graph databases	GDB1, GDB2, . . . , GDB6
Graph pictures	Pic1, Pic2, . . . , Pic6
System variables	Xmin, Xmax, and others

Programs have user-defined names also and share memory with variables. Programs are entered and edited from the program editor (Chapter 13).

You can store to matrices (Chapter 10), lists (Chapter 11), system variables such as **Xmax** (Chapter 3) or **TblMin** (Chapter 7), and all functions (Chapters 3, 4, 5, and 6) from the Home screen or from a program. You can store to matrices (Chapter 10), lists (Chapter 12), and functions (Chapter 3) from editors. You can store to a matrix element (Chapter 10) or a list element (Chapter 11). Graph databases and pictures are stored and recalled using instructions from the DRAW menu (Chapter 8).

Storing and Recalling Variable Values

Values are stored to and recalled from memory using variable names. When an expression containing the name of a variable is evaluated, the value of the variable at that time is used.

Storing Values in a Variable

You can store a value to a variable from the Home screen or a program using the $\boxed{\text{STO}\blacktriangleright}$ key. Begin on a blank line.

1. Enter the value that you want to store (which can be an expression).

2. Press $\boxed{\text{STO}\blacktriangleright}$. The symbol → is copied to the cursor location.

3. Press $\boxed{\text{ALPHA}}$, then the letter of the variable to which you want to store the value.

4. Press $\boxed{\text{ENTER}}$. If you entered an expression, it is evaluated. The value is stored in the variable.

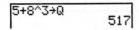

Displaying a Variable Value

To display the value of a variable, enter the name on a blank line on the Home screen, and press $\boxed{\text{ENTER}}$.

RCL (Recall)

You can copy variable contents to the current cursor location. Press $\boxed{\text{2nd}}$ [RCL], and then enter the name of the variable in one of the following ways:

• Press $\boxed{\text{ALPHA}}$ and then the letter of the variable.

• Press $\boxed{\text{2nd}}$ and the name of the list.

• Press $\boxed{\text{MATRX}}$ and select the name of the matrix.

• Press $\boxed{\text{2nd}}$ [Y-VARS] and select the type and name of the function.

• Press $\boxed{\text{PRGM}}$ and select the name of the program (in the program editor only).

You can edit the characters copied to the expression without affecting the value in memory.

Note: When an error (such as a variable with no assigned value) occurs on the RCL line, the name is cleared automatically for you to enter the correct name. To leave RCL without recalling a value, press $\boxed{\text{CLEAR}}$.

Last Entry

When you press ENTER on the Home screen to evaluate an expression or execute an instruction, the expression or instruction is stored in a storage area called Last Entry, which you can recall. When you turn the TI-82 off, Last Entry is retained in memory.

Using Last Entry

You can recall Last Entry and edit it from the Home screen or any editor. Press 2nd [ENTRY]. On the Home screen or a numeric editor, the current line is cleared and the Last Entry is copied to the line. The cursor is positioned at the end of the entry. In the program editor, the Last Entry is inserted at the cursor location. Because the TI-82 updates the Last Entry storage area only when ENTER is pressed, you can recall the previous entry even if you have begun entering the next expression. However, when you recall Last Entry, it replaces what you have typed.

5 + 7	5+7
ENTER	12
2nd [ENTRY]	5+7■

Multiple Entries on a Line

To enter more than one expression or instruction on a line, separate them with a colon (:). They are all stored together in Last Entry (page 1-14).

If the previous entry contained more than one expression or instruction, separated with a colon (page 1-7), they all are recalled. You can recall all entries on a line, edit any of them, and then execute all of them.

Using the equation $A=\pi r^2$, use trial and error to find the radius of a circle that covers 200 square centimeters. Use 8 as your first guess.

8 STO▸ ALPHA R 2nd [:]	8→R:πR²
2nd [π] ALPHA R x^2	201.0619298
ENTER	8→R:πR²■
2nd [ENTRY]	

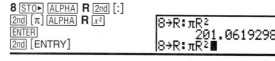

2nd ◄ 7 2nd [INS] .95	8→R:πR² 201.0619298 7.95→R:πR² 198.5565097
ENTER	

Continue until the answer is as accurate as you want.

Reexecuting the Previous Entry

To execute Last Entry press [ENTER] on a blank line on the Home screen; the entry does not display again.

0 [STO▶] [ALPHA] **N** [ENTER] [ALPHA] **N** [+] **1** [STO▶] [ALPHA] **N** [2nd] [:] [ALPHA] **N** [x^2] [ENTER] [ENTER] [ENTER]	0→N
	                    0
	N+1→N:N²
	                    1
	                    4
	                    9

Accessing a Previous Entry

The TI-82 retains as many of the previous entries as is possible (up to a total of 128 bytes) in the Last Entry storage area. You can access those entries by continuing to press [2nd] [ENTRY]. (If a single entry is more than 128 bytes, it is retained for Last Entry, but it cannot be placed in the Last Entry storage area.)

1 [STO▶] [ALPHA] **A** [ENTER] 2 [STO▶] [ALPHA] **B** [ENTER] 3 [STO▶] [ALPHA] **C** [ENTER] [2nd] [ENTRY]	1→A
	                    1
	2→B
	                    2
	3→C
	                    3
	3→C■

Each time you press [2nd] [ENTRY], the current line is overwritten. If you press [2nd] [ENTRY] after displaying the oldest item, the newest item is displayed.

[2nd] [ENTRY]	1→A
	                    1
	2→B
	                    2
	3→C
	                    3
	2→B■

Last Answer

When an expression is evaluated successfully from the Home screen or from a program, the TI-82 stores the answer to a variable, Ans (Last Answer). Ans may be a real number, a list, or a matrix. When you turn the TI-82 off, the value in Ans is retained in memory.

Using Ans in an Expression

You can use the variable **Ans** to represent the last answer in most places. Press [2nd] [ANS] and the variable name **Ans** is copied to the cursor location. When the expression is evaluated, the TI-82 uses the value of **Ans** in the calculation.

Calculate the area of a garden plot 1.7 meters by 4.2 meters. Then calculate the yield per square meter if the plot produces a total of 147 tomatoes.

1.7 [×] **4.2**	
[ENTER]	
147 [÷] [2nd] [ANS]	
[ENTER]	

```
1.7*4.2
              7.14
147/Ans
         20.58823529
```

Continuing an Expression

You can use the value in **Ans** as the first entry in the next expression without entering the value again or pressing [2nd] [ANS]. On the blank line on the Home screen, enter the function. The TI-82 "types" the variable name **Ans** followed by the function.

5 [÷] **2**	
[ENTER]	
[×] **9.9**	
[ENTER]	

```
5/2
               2.5
Ans*9.9
             24.75
```

Storing Answers

To store an answer, store **Ans** to a variable before you evaluate another expression.

Calculate the area of a circle of radius 5 meters. Then calculate the volume of a cylinder of radius 5 meters and height 3.3 meters and store in the variable **V**.

[2nd] [π] **5** [x^2]	
[ENTER]	
[×] **3.3**	
[ENTER]	
[STO▶] [ALPHA] **V**	
[ENTER]	

```
π5²
        78.53981634
Ans*3.3
       259.1813939
Ans→V
       259.1813939
```

TI-82 Menus

To leave the keyboard uncluttered, the TI-82 uses full-screen menus to access many operations. The use of specific menus is described in the appropriate chapters.

Moving from One Menu to Another

A menu key may access more than one menu. The names of the menus appear on the top line. The current menu is highlighted and the items in that menu are displayed.

Use ▶ or ◀ to move the cursor to a different menu.

Selecting an Item from a Menu

The number of the current item is highlighted. If there are more than seven items on the menu, a ↓ appears on the last line in place of the : (colon). Menu items that end in ... (ellipsis marks) access another menu.

There are two methods of selecting from a menu.

- Press the number of the item you want to select.

- Use ▼ and ▲ to move the cursor to the item you want to select and then press [ENTER].

Leaving a Menu without Making a Selection

After you make a selection from a menu, you usually are returned to the screen where you were.

To leave a menu without making a selection, do any of the following:

- Press [2nd] [QUIT] to return to the Home screen.

- Press [CLEAR] to return to the screen where you were.

- Display a different menu by pressing the appropriate key, such as [MATH].

- Select another screen by pressing the appropriate key, such as [WINDOW].

Calculate $6^3\sqrt{27}$.

1. Press **6**. Press MATH to display the MATH menu.

2. To select $^3\sqrt{}$, you may either press **4** or press ▼ ▼ ▼
   ENTER.

3. Press **27** and then press ENTER to evaluate the
   expression.

```
6³√27
              18
```

VARS and Y-VARS Menus

Occasionally you may want to access the names of
functions and system variables to use in an expression
or to store to them directly. Use the VARS or Y-VARS
menus to access the names of variables such as Xmin
and functions such Y1.

VARS Menu

The VARS menu accesses the names of WINDOW variables
such as **Xmin** and **Tstep**, the user-defined ZOOM variables
such as **ZXmin**, graph databases and graph pictures such as
GDB1 and **Pic2**, statistics variables such as $\bar{x}$, **RegEQ** and
Q1, and table variables such as **TblMin**.

Press [VARS] to display the VARS menu. Some of the items
access more than one menu of variable names.

VARS	
1: Window...	Names of X/Y, T/θ, U/V variables
2: Zoom...	Names of ZX/ZY, ZT/Zθ, ZU variables
3: GDB...	Names of **GDB***n* variables
4: Picture...	Names of **Pic***n* variables
5: Statistics...	X/Y, Σ, EQ, BOX, PTS variables
6: Table...	Names of Table variables

Y-VARS Menu

The Y-VARS menu accesses the names of functions and the
instructions to select or deselect functions from a program
or the Home screen.

Press [2nd] [Y-VARS] to display the Y-VARS menu.

Y-VARS	
1: Function...	Displays names of **Y***n* functions
2: Parametric...	Displays names of **X***n*T, **Y***n*T functions
3: Polar...	Displays names of **r***n* functions
4: Sequence...	Displays names of **U***n*, **V***n* functions
5: On/Off...	Lets you select/deselect functions

**Accessing a
Name from a
VARS or
Y-VARS Menu**

1. Press [VARS] or [2nd] [Y-VARS]. The VARS or Y-VARS
   menu is displayed.

2. Select the type of name you want; **Picture...** or **Polar...**,
   for example.

   • In VARS, use [▶] or [◀] to move to the menu you
     want, if necessary.

   • In Y-VARS, a single menu is displayed.

3. Select the name you want from the menu. It is copied to
   the cursor location.

EOS (Equation Operating System)

The Equation Operating System (EOS™) defines the order in which functions in expressions are entered and evaluated on the TI-82. EOS lets you enter numbers and functions in a simple, straightforward sequence.

Order of Evaluation

A function returns a value. EOS evaluates the functions in an expression in the following order:

1	Functions that are entered after the argument, such as ^{2}, $^{-1}$, !, $°$, ^{r}, ^{T}, and conversions.
2	Powers and roots, such as $2\wedge5$ or $5^x\sqrt{32}$.
3	Implied multiplication where the second argument is a number, variable name, list, or matrix or begins with an open parenthesis, such as **4A**, **3[B]**, **(A+B)4**, or **4(A+B)**.
4	Single-argument functions that precede the argument, such as negation, $\sqrt{\ }$, **sin**, or **log**.
5	Implied multiplication where the second argument is a multiargument function or a single-argument function that precedes the argument, such as **2nDeriv(A²,A,6)** or **Asin 2**.
6	Permutations (**nPr**) and combinations (**nCr**).
7	Multiplication and division.
8	Addition and subtraction.
9	Relational functions, such as **>** or ≤.
10	Logic operator **and**.
11	Logic operators **or** and **xor**.

Within a priority group, EOS evaluates functions from left to right. However, two or more single-argument functions that precede the same argument are evaluated from right to left. For example, **sin fPart ln 8** is evaluated as **sin(fPart(ln 8))**.

Calculations within a pair of parentheses are evaluated first. Multiargument functions, such as **nDeriv(A²,A,6)**, are evaluated as they are encountered.

Implied Multiplication	The TI-82 recognizes implied multiplication. For example, it understands 2π, **4 sin 46**, **5(1+2)**, and **(2*5)7** as implied multiplication.
Parentheses	All calculations inside a pair of parentheses are completed first. For example, in the expression **4(1+2)**, EOS first evaluates the portion inside the parentheses, **1+2**, and then multiplies the answer, **3**, by **4**.

You can omit any right (close) parenthesis at the end of an expression. All "open" parenthetical elements are closed automatically at the end of an expression and preceding the → (store) or display conversion instructions.

Note: If the name of a list or matrix is followed by an open parenthesis, it does not indicate implied multiplication. It is used to access specific elements in the list (Chapter 11) or matrix (Chapter 10).

Negation

To enter a negative number, use the negation function. Press ⎡(-)⎤ and then enter the number. On the TI-82, negation is in the fourth group in the EOS hierarchy. Functions in the first group, such as squaring, are evaluated before negation.

For example, **-X^2** is a negative number (or 0); **-9^2** is **-81**. Use parentheses to square a negative number: **(-9)^2**.

```
-2²
                    -4
(-2)²
                     4
-A²
                    -4
(-A)²
                     4
```

Note: Use the ⎡-⎤ key for subtraction and the ⎡(-)⎤ key for negation. If you press ⎡-⎤ to enter a negative number, as in **9** ⎡×⎤ ⎡-⎤ **7**, or if you press ⎡(-)⎤ to indicate subtraction, as in **9** ⎡(-)⎤ **7**, it is an error. If you press ⎡ALPHA⎤ **A** ⎡(-)⎤ ⎡ALPHA⎤ **B**, it is interpreted as implied multiplication (**A*-B**).

Error Conditions

The TI-82 detects any errors at the time it evaluates an expression, executes an instruction, plots a graph, or stores a value. Calculations stop and an error message with a menu displays immediately. Error codes and conditions are described in detail in Appendix B.

Diagnosing an Error

If the TI-82 detects an error, it displays the error screen.

The top line indicates the general type of error, such as SYNTAX or DOMAIN. Additional information about each error message is in Appendix B.

• If you select **Goto**, the cursor is displayed at the location where the error was detected.

   Note: If a syntax error was detected in the contents of a Y= function during program execution, this option returns the user to the Y= editor, not the program.

• If you select **Quit** or press [2nd] [QUIT] or [CLEAR], you return to the Home screen.

Correcting an Error

1. Note the type of the error.

2. Select **Goto**, if that option is available, and look at the expression for syntax errors, especially at and in front of the cursor location.

3. If the error in the expression is not readily apparent, turn to Appendix B and read the information about the error message.

4. Correct the expression.

Chapter 2: Math, Angle, and Test Operations

This chapter describes math, angle, and relational operations that are available on the TI-82. The most commonly used functions are accessed from the keyboard; others are accessed through full-screen menus.

Chapter Contents

Getting Started: Lottery Chances

Getting Started is a fast-paced introduction. Read the chapter for details.

Suppose you want to enter a lottery where 6 numbers will be drawn out of 49. To win, you must pick all 6 numbers (in any order). What is the probability of winning if you buy one ticket? What is the probability of winning if you buy five tickets?

1. Determine the number of combinations possible. On the Home screen, press **49** to enter the total number of items. Press [MATH] ◀ to display the MATH PRB menu. Press **3** or ▼ ▼ [ENTER] to select **nCr**. Press **6** to enter the number of items selected.

```
49 nCr 6
           13983816
```

2. Press [ENTER] to evaluate the expression. This is the total number of possible combinations of 6 numbers drawn from a set of 49 numbers. With one ticket, you have one chance in 13,983,816 of winning.

3. To calculate the probability of winning with one ticket, press **1** ÷ [2nd] [ANS] [ENTER]. The answer is expressed in scientific notation on the TI-82 because it is so small. The decimal equivalent is 0.00000007151123842.

```
49 nCr 6
           13983816
1/Ans
    7.151123842ᴇ⁻8
```

4. To calculate the probability of winning with five tickets, press × **5** [ENTER]. Again, the answer is too small to display in fixed notation. The decimal equivalent is 0.0000003575561921.

```
49 nCr 6
           13983816
1/Ans
    7.151123842ᴇ⁻8
Ans*5
    3.575561921ᴇ⁻7
```

Keyboard Math Operations

The most commonly used math functions are on the keyboard.

Using Lists with Functions	Functions that are valid for lists return a list calculated on an element-by-element basis. If two lists are used in the same expression, they must be the same length.

```
{1,2}+{3,4}+5
           {9 11}
```

+ (Add) **– (Subtract)** *** (Multiply)** **/ (Divide)**	+ (addition $\boxed{+}$), – (subtraction $\boxed{-}$), * (multiplication $\boxed{\times}$), and / (division $\boxed{\div}$) may be used with numbers, expressions, lists, or matrices (Chapter 10).

valueA+*valueB*, *valueA*–*valueB*,
valueA*valueB, *valueA*/*valueB*

Trig Functions	The trigonometric functions may be used with numbers, expressions, or lists. They are interpreted according to the current **Radian/Degree** MODE setting. For example, **sin 30** in **Radian** MODE returns **-.9880316241**; in **Degree** MODE it returns **.5**.

sin *value*, **cos** *value*, **tan** *value*

sin⁻¹, **cos⁻¹**, and **tan⁻¹** are the inverse trig functions (arcsine, arccosine, and arctangent).

sin⁻¹ *value*, **cos⁻¹** *value*, **tan⁻¹** *value*

^ (Power) **2 (Square)** **√ (Square Root)**	^ (power $\boxed{\wedge}$), ² (squared $\boxed{x^2}$), and √ (square root $\boxed{\text{2nd}}$ $[\sqrt{\ }]$) may be used with numbers, expressions, lists, or matrices (Chapter 10).

value^*power*, *value*², √*value*

Note: Raising a negative number to a noninteger power can result in a complex number, which returns an error.

⁻¹ (Inverse)	⁻¹ (inverse $\boxed{x^{-1}}$) may be used with numbers, expressions, lists, or matrices (Chapter 10).The multiplicative inverse is the equivalent of the reciprocal, 1/x.

value⁻¹

```
5⁻¹
              .2
```

Keyboard Math Operations (Continued)

---

log
10^
ln

log (logarithm [LOG]), **10^** (power of ten [2nd] [10ˣ]), and ln (natural log [2nd] [ln]) may be used with a number, expression, or list.

log *value*, **10^***power*, ln *value*

e^

e^ (exponential [2nd] [eˣ]) may be used with a number, expression, or list. **e^** returns the constant e raised to a power. **e^1** returns the value of the constant e.

e^*power*

```
e^5
     148.4131591
e^1
     2.718281828
```

⁻ (Negation)

⁻ (negation [(-)]) returns the negative of a number, expression, list, or matrix (Chapter 10). The narrow negation symbol (⁻) distinguishes negation from the subtraction or minus [–] (–).

⁻*value*

EOS rules (Chapter 1) determine when negation is evaluated. For example, ⁻**A**^{2} returns a negative number (squaring is evaluated before negation according to EOS rules). Use parentheses to square a negated number, (⁻**A**)^2.

```
2→A: {-A², (-A)², -
2², (-2)²}
       {-4 4 -4 4}
```

abs

abs (absolute value) returns the absolute value of a number, expression, list, or matrix (Chapter 10).

abs *value*

π (Pi)

Pi is stored as a constant in the TI-82. Press [2nd] [π] to copy the symbol π to the cursor location. The number 3.1415926535898 is used internally in calculations.

MATH MATH Operations

To display the MATH MATH menu, press $\boxed{\text{MATH}}$. When you select an item from the menu, the name is copied to the cursor location. Functions that are valid for lists return a list calculated on an element-by-element basis.

MATH MATH Menu

MATH NUM HYP PRB

1: ▶Frac	Display answer as fraction
2: ▶Dec	Display answer as decimal
3: ^{3}	Cube
4: $^3\sqrt{\ }$	Cube root
5: $^x\sqrt{\ }$	n^{th} root
6: fMin(	Minimum of a function
7: fMax(	Maximum of a function
8: nDeriv(	Numerical derivative
9: fnInt(	Function integral
0: solve(	Solution (root) of a function

▶Frac

▶Frac (display as fraction) displays an answer as the rational equivalent. The answer may be a number, expression, list, or matrix. If it cannot be simplified or the denominator is more than three digits, the decimal equivalent is returned. **▶Frac** is valid only at the end of an expression.

expression▶**Frac**

```
1/2+1/3▶Frac
              5/6
```

▶Dec

▶Dec (display as decimal) displays an answer in decimal form. **▶Dec** is valid only at the end of an expression.

expression▶**Dec**

```
1/2+1/3▶Frac
              5/6
Ans▶Dec
     .8333333333
```

³ (Cube)

³ (cube, MATH MATH item 3) returns the cube of a number, expression, list, or square matrix (Chapter 10).

$value^3$

```
{2,3,4,5}³
    {8 27 64 125}
```

³√ (Cube Root)

³√ (cube root, MATH MATH item 4) returns the cube root of a number, expression, or list.

$\sqrt[3]{value}$

```
³√{8,27,64,125}
     {2 3 4 5}
```

ˣ√ (Root)

ˣ√ (root, MATH MATH item 5) returns the nth real root of a number, expression, or list.

$n^{th}root^x\sqrt{value}$

```
5 ˣ√32
                2
```

fMin(
fMax(

fMin((function minimum, MATH MATH item 6) and **fMax(** (function maximum, MATH MATH item 7) return the value at which the minimum or maximum value of *expression* with respect to *variable* occurs, between *lower* and *upper* values for *variable*. *lower* must be less than *upper*. **fMin(** and **fMax(** are not valid in *expression*. The accuracy is controlled by *tolerance* (optional; if not specified, 1ᴇ⁻5 is used). If there is no finite minimum or maximum in the interval, usually (depending on *expression*) an error occurs.

fMin(*expression,variable,lower,upper***)** or
fMin(*expression,variable,lower,upper,tolerance***)**

```
fMin(sin A,A, ⁻π,
π)
     -1.570797171
```

nDeriv(

nDeriv((numerical derivative, MATH MATH item 8) returns an approximate derivative of *expression* with respect to *variable*, given the *value* at which to calculate the derivative, and ε (optional; if none is specified, 1ε⁻3 is used).

nDeriv(*expression,variable,value***)** or
nDeriv(*expression,variable,value,*ε**)**

nDeriv(uses the symmetric difference quotient method, which approximates the numerical derivative value as the slope of the secant line through the points:

$(value-\varepsilon, expression(value-\varepsilon))$ and
$(value+\varepsilon, expression(value+\varepsilon))$

As ε gets smaller, the approximation usually gets more accurate.

```
nDeriv(A^3,A,5,.
01)
          75.0001
nDeriv(A^3,A,5,.
0001)
               75
```

nDeriv(can be used once in *expression*. Because of the method, nDeriv(can return a false derivative value at a nondifferentiable point.

fnInt(

fnInt((function integral, MATH MATH item 9) returns the numerical integral (Gauss-Kronrod method) of *expression* with respect to *variable*, given *lower* limit, *upper* limit, and a *tolerance* (optional; if none is specified, 1ε⁻5 is used).

fnInt(*expression,variable,lower,upper***)** or
fnInt(*expression,variable,lower,upper,tolerance***)**

```
fnInt(A²,A,0,1)
      .3333333333
```

fnInt(is not valid in *expression*.

solve(

solve((MATH MATH item 0) returns a solution (root) of *expression* for *variable*, given an initial *guess*, a *lower* bound, and an *upper* bound within which a solution is sought (optional, if not specified, *lower*=⁻1E99 and *upper*=1E99).

solve(*expression*,*variable*,*guess***)** or
solve(*expression*,*variable*,*guess*,{*lower*,*upper*}**)**

expression is assumed equal to zero. The value of *variable* in memory will not be updated. *guess* may be a value or a list of two values. Values must be stored to every variable in *expression*, except *variable*, before *expression* is evaluated. *lower* and *upper* are entered in list format.

```
solve(Q^3-125,Q,
4,{0,100})
                5
```

Controlling the Solution for solve(

The TI-82 solves equations through an iterative process. To control that process, you should provide a close bound of the solution and at least one initial guess (which must be within the bounds). This will help to:

• Find a solution.

• Define which solution you want for equations with multiple solutions.

• Find the solution more quickly.

MATH NUM (Number) Operations

To display the MATH NUM menu, press MATH ▷. When you select an item from the menu, the name is copied to the cursor location. Functions that are valid for lists return a list calculated on an element-by-element basis.

MATH NUM Menu

```
MATH NUM HYP PRB
1:round(          Round
2:iPart           Integer part
3:fPart           Fractional part
4:int             Greatest integer
5:min(            Minimum value
6:max(            Maximum value
```

round(

round(returns a number, expression, list, or matrix rounded to #*decimals* (≤ 9). If #*decimals* is omitted, *value* is rounded to 10 digits.

round(*value*,#*decimals***)**
round(*value***)**

```
round(π,3)
           3.142
```

iPart

iPart (integer part) returns the integer part or parts of a number, expression, list, or matrix (Chapter 10).

iPart *value*

fPart

fPart (fractional part) returns the fractional part or parts of a number, expression, list, or matrix (Chapter 10).

fPart *value*

```
iPart -23.45
             -23
fPart -23.45
             -.45
```

int

int (greatest integer) returns the largest integer less than or equal to a number, expression, list, or matrix. The value is the same as **iPart** for nonnegative numbers and negative integers, but one integer less than **iPart** for negative noninteger numbers.

int *value*

```
int -23.45
           -24
```

min(
max(

min((minimum value) returns the smaller of *valueA* or *valueB* or the smallest element in a list. If two lists are compared, it returns a list of the smaller of each pair of elements.

max((maximum value) returns the larger of *valueA* or *valueB* or the largest element in a list. If two lists are compared, it returns a list of the larger of each pair of elements.

min(*valueA*,*valueB*) or max(*valueA*,*valueB*)
min(*list*) or max(*list*)
min(*listA*,*listB*) or max(*listA*,*listB*)

```
max(-7,9/2)
            4.5
max({1,2,3})
              3
max({1,2,3},{3,2
,1})
        {3 2 3}
```

Note: The min(and max(functions on the MATH NUM menu are the same as the min(and max(functions on the LIST MATH menu.

MATH HYP (Hyperbolic) Operations

To display the MATH HYP menu, press $\boxed{\text{MATH}}$ $\boxed{\triangleright}$ $\boxed{\triangleright}$. When you select an item from the menu, the name is copied to the cursor location. Functions that are valid for lists return a list calculated on an element-by-element basis.

MATH HYP Menu

```
MATH NUM HYP PRB
1:sinh            Hyperbolic sine
2:cosh            Hyperbolic cosine
3:tanh            Hyperbolic tangent
4:sinh⁻¹          Hyperbolic arcsine
5:cosh⁻¹          Hyperbolic arccosine
6:tanh⁻¹          Hyperbolic arctangent
```

**sinh
cosh
tanh**

sinh, **cosh**, and **tanh** are the hyperbolic functions. They are valid for lists.

sinh *value*

```
sinh .5
       .5210953055
```

**sinh⁻¹
cosh⁻¹
tanh⁻¹**

sinh⁻¹, **cosh⁻¹**, and **tanh⁻¹** are the hyperbolic arcsine, hyperbolic arccosine, and hyperbolic arctangent functions, respectively. They are valid for lists.

sinh⁻¹ *value*

```
sinh⁻¹ {0,1}
      {0 .881373587}
```

MATH PRB (Probability) Operations

To display the MATH PRB menu, press [MATH] [◄]. When you select an item from the menu, the name is copied to the cursor location. Functions that are valid for lists return a list calculated on an element-by-element basis.

MATH PRB Menu

```
MATH NUM HYP PRB
1: rand          Random number generator
2: nPr           Number of permutations
3: nCr           Number of combinations
4: !             Factorial
```

rand

rand (random number) generates and returns a random number greater than 0 and less than 1. A random number is generated from a seed value. To control a random number sequence, first store an integer seed value in **rand**. If you store **0** to **rand**, the TI-82 uses the factory-set seed value. When you reset the TI-82, **rand** is set to the factory seed.

```
0→rand:rand*3
          2.830792207
```

nPr

nPr (number of permutations) returns the number of permutations of *items* taken *number* at a time. *items* and *number* must be nonnegative integers.

items **nPr** *number*

nCr

nCr (number of combinations) returns the number of combinations of *items* taken *number* at a time. *items* and *number* must be nonnegative integers.

items **nCr** *number*

```
5 nPr 2
              20
5 nCr 2
              10
```

! (Factorial)

! (factorial) returns the factorial of a positive integer between 0 and 69.

*value***!**

```
6!
             720
```

ANGLE Operations

To display the ANGLE menu, press [2nd] [ANGLE]. The
ANGLE menu displays angle indicators and instructions.
When you select an item from the menu, the name is
copied to the cursor location. Angle entries are
interpreted according to the Radian/Degree MODE
setting.

**ANGLE
Menu**

```
ANGLE
1:°                   Degree function
2:'                   DMS entry notation
3:r                   Radian function
4:▶DMS                Display as degree/minute/second
5:R▶Pr(               Returns R, given X and Y
6:R▶Pθ(               Returns θ, given X and Y
7:P▶Rx(               Returns X, given R and θ
8:P▶Ry(               Returns Y, given R and θ
```

Note: Do not enter DMS numbers as **54°32'30"** on the
TI-82. **54°32'** is interpreted as implied multiplication of
54° and 32', and " is a quote mark used to enter text.

°(Degree)

°(degree) lets you designate *angle* as degree, regardless of
the current angle MODE setting. *angle* may be a list.

angle°

**' (DMS Entry
Notation)**

' (DMS entry notation) lets you enter degrees, minutes, and
seconds in DMS format.

degrees'minutes'seconds'

For example, enter **30'1'23'** for 30 degrees, 1 minute,
23 seconds. Note that the MODE setting must be **Degree** (or
you must use the **Degree** function) for the TI-82 to
interpret the argument as degrees, minutes, and seconds.

```
sin 30'1'23'
        .5003484441
```
Degree MODE

```
sin 30'1'23'
        -.9842129995
sin 30'1'23'°
        .5003484441
```
Radian MODE

r (Radians)

r (radian) lets you designate *angle* as radian, regardless of
the current angle MODE setting. *angle* may be a list.

*angle*r

ANGLE Operations (Continued)

▸DMS

▸**DMS** (display as degree/minute/second) displays *answer* in degree, minute, second format. The MODE setting must be **Degree** for the TI-82 to interpret *answer* as degrees, minutes, and seconds. ▸**DMS** is valid only at the end of a line.

answer▸**DMS**

```
54'32'30'*2
       109.0833333
Ans▸DMS
         109°5'0"
```

R▸Pr (
R▸Pθ(
P▸Rx(
P▸Ry(

R▸Pr (converts rectangular to polar and returns **R**, and **R▸Pθ(** converts rectangular to polar and returns θ, given X and Y rectangular coordinate values.

R▸Pr(*X*,*Y*)
R▸Pθ(*X*,*Y*)

```
R▸Pr(-1,0)
              1
R▸Pθ(-1,0)
     3.141592654
```

P▸Rx(converts polar to rectangular and returns **X**, and **P▸Ry(** converts polar to rectangular and returns **Y**, given R and θ polar coordinate values.

P▸Rx(*R*,θ)
P▸Ry(*R*,θ)

```
P▸Rx(1,π)
             -1
P▸Ry(1,π)
              0
```

TEST TEST (Relational) Operations

To display the TEST TEST menu, press [2nd] [TEST]. When you select from the menu, the name is copied to the cursor location. These functions are valid for lists; they return a list calculated on an element-by-element basis.

TEST TEST Menu

TEST	LOGIC	**True if:**
1: =		Equal
2: ≠		Not equal to
3: >		Greater than
4: ≥		Greater than or equal to
5: <		Less than
6: ≤		Less than or equal to

=
≠
>
≥
<
≤

Relational operators compare *valueA* and *valueB* and return **1** if the test is true or **0** if the test is false. *valueA* and *valueB* can be numbers, expressions, lists, or matrices (Chapter 10), but they must match in type and dimension. Relational operators are often used in programs to control program flow and in graphing to control the graph of a function over specific values.

valueA=valueB

```
{1,2,3}={3,2,1}
            {0 1 0}
{1,2,3}≠{3,2,1}
            {1 0 1}
{1,2,3}<{3,2,1}
            {1 0 0}
```

Using Tests

Relational operators are evaluated after mathematical functions according to EOS rules (Chapter 1).

- The expression **2+2=2+3** returns **0**. The TI-82 does the addition first because of EOS rules, and then it compares 4 to 5.

- The expression **2+(2=2)+3** returns **6**. The TI-82 first performs the relational test because it is in parentheses, and then it adds 2, 1, and 3.

TEST LOGIC (Boolean) Operations

To display the TEST LOGIC menu, press [2nd] [TEST] [▶].
When you select from the menu, the name is copied to
the cursor location.

TEST LOGIC Menu	TEST LOGIC 1: and 2: or 3: xor 4: not	**True if:** Both values are nonzero (true) At least one value is nonzero (true) Only one value is zero (false) The value is zero (true)

Boolean Operators

Boolean operators are often used in programs to control
program flow and in graphing to control the graph of a
function over specific values. Values are interpreted as
zero (false) or nonzero (true).

and
or
xor

and, **or**, and **xor** (exclusive or) return a value of **1** if a
expression is true or **0** if the expression is false, according
to the table below. *valueA* and *valueB* can be expressions.

valueA **and** *valueB*
valueA **or** *valueB*
valueA **xor** *valueB*

valueA	*valueB*		**and**	**or**	**xor**
$\neq 0$	$\neq 0$	returns	1	1	0
$\neq 0$	0	returns	0	1	1
0	$\neq 0$	returns	0	1	1
0	0	returns	0	0	0

not

not returns 1 if *value* (which can be an expression) is 0.

not *value*

Using Boolean Operations

Boolean logic is often used with relational tests. In a
program, the following instructions store **4** into **C**:

```
PROGRAM:BOOLEAN
:2→A:3→B
:If A=2 and B=3
:Then:4→C
:Else:5→C
:End
```

Chapter 3: Function Graphing

This chapter describes function graphing on the TI-82 in detail. It also lays the foundation for using the other graphing features of the TI-82.

Chapter Contents

Getting Started: Graphing a Circle

Getting Started is a fast-paced introduction. Read the chapter for details.

Graph a circle of radius 10, centered on the origin in the standard viewing window. To graph a circle, you must enter separate formulas for the upper and lower portions of the circle. Then use ZOOM Square to adjust the display to make the functions appear as a circle.

1. In **Func** MODE, press $\boxed{\text{Y=}}$ to display the Y= edit screen. Press $\boxed{\text{2nd}}$ $[\sqrt{\ }]$ $\boxed{(}$ **100** $\boxed{-}$ $\boxed{\text{X,T,}\Theta}$ $\boxed{x^2}$ $\boxed{)}$ $\boxed{\text{ENTER}}$ to enter the expression to define the top half of the circle, $Y_1=\sqrt{(100-X^2)}$.

   The bottom half of the circle is defined by $Y_2=-\sqrt{(100-X^2)}$. However, on the TI-82 you can define one function in terms of another, so to define $Y_2=-Y_1$, press $\boxed{(-)}$ $\boxed{\text{2nd}}$ [Y-VARS] (to display the Y= variables menu) **1** (to select **Function...**) **1** (to select **Y₁**).

```
\Y1=√(100-X²)
\Y2=-Y1
\Y3=
\Y4=
\Y5=
\Y6=
\Y7=
\Y8=
```

2. Press $\boxed{\text{ZOOM}}$ and then select **ZStandard**. This is a quick way to reset the WINDOW variables to the standard values. It also graphs the functions; you do not need to press $\boxed{\text{GRAPH}}$.

   Notice that the functions appear as an ellipse in the standard viewing window.

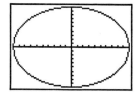

3. To adjust the display so each "dot" represents an equal width and height, press $\boxed{\text{ZOOM}}$ and then select **ZSquare**. The functions are replotted and now appear as a circle on the display.

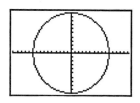

4. To see the effect of **ZSquare** on the WINDOW variables, press $\boxed{\text{WINDOW}}$ and notice the new values for **Xmin, Xmax, Ymin**, and **Ymax**.

```
WINDOW FORMAT
Xmin=-15.16129...
Xmax=15.161290...
Xscl=1
Ymin=-10
Ymax=10
Yscl=1
```

Defining a Graph

To define a graph, you set the modes, enter and select the functions to graph, and define the viewing WINDOW and WINDOW FORMAT. Once you have defined a graph, you can plot, display, and explore it.

Steps in Defining a Graph

There are six basic steps to defining a graph. You may not need to do all the steps each time you define a graph. The procedures are described in detail on the following pages.

1. Set the MODE to **Func** graphing.

2. Enter or edit a function in the Y= list.

3. Select the Y= function you want to graph.

4. Define the viewing WINDOW variables.

5. Set the WINDOW FORMAT.

6. Deselect stat plots, if appropriate (Chapter 12.)

Exploring a Graph

Once you have defined a graph, you can display it and then use several tools of the TI-82 to explore the behavior of the function or functions. These tools are described later in this chapter.

Saving a Graph

You can store the elements that define the current graph in one of six graph databases (Chapter 8). Later, you can recall that database to recreate the current graph.

You can store a picture of the current graph display in one of six graph pictures (Chapter 8). Later, you can superimpose that picture on the current graph.

Setting Graph Modes

Pressing [MODE] displays the current MODE settings
(Chapter 1). The graphing MODE in function graphing
must be Func.

Checking and Changing Graphing Modes

Press [MODE] to display the MODE settings. The current
settings are highlighted.

The TI-82 has four graphing modes.

- **Func** (function graphing)
- **Par** (parametric graphing)
- **Pol** (polar graphing)
- **Seq** (sequence graphing)

To graph functions, you must select **Func** (function
graphing). The basics of graphing on the TI-82 are
described in this chapter. Differences in parametric
graphing (Chapter 4), polar graphing (Chapter 5), and
sequence graphing (Chapter 6) are described in those
chapters.

Radian or **Degree** MODE may affect how some functions
are interpreted. **Connected** or **Dot** affects how the selected
functions are plotted. **Sequential** or **Simul** affects how
functions are plotted if you have more than one function
selected.

Setting Modes from a Program

You may set the graphing mode and other modes from a
program.

Begin on a blank line in the program editor. Press [MODE] to
display the interactive MODE selection screen. Use ▼, ▲,
▶, and ◀ to place the cursor on the MODE that you want
to select, and press [ENTER]. The name of the MODE is
copied to the cursor location.

Defining Functions in the Y= List

Pressing Y= accesses the Y= edit screen, where you enter the functions to graph. You can store up to ten functions in memory at one time. You can graph one or more of these functions at a time.

Displaying the Functions in the Y= List

Press Y= to display the Y= edit screen. In the example below, the **Y1** and **Y2** functions are defined.

```
Y1◻√(100-X²)
Y2◻-Y1
Y3=
Y4=
Y5=
Y6=
Y7=
Y8=
```

Defining a New Function

To define a new function, enter an expression on the Y= edit screen.

1. Move the cursor to the function in the Y= list you want to define. If necessary, press CLEAR to erase a previously entered function.

2. Enter the expression to define the function.

   • You may use functions and variables (including matrices and lists) in the expression. If the expression evaluates to a value that is not a real number, that point is not plotted; an error does not occur.

   • The independent variable in the function is **X**. You may press X,T,Θ, rather than pressing ALPHA [X], for the **X** variable. (**Func** MODE defines the independent variable as **X**.)

   • The expression is stored as one of the ten user-defined functions in the Y= list as you enter it.

3. When you complete the expression, press ENTER to move to the beginning of the next function.

Defining Functions in the Y= List (Continued)

Editing a Function	1. Move the cursor to the function in the Y= list you want to change.
	2. Make the changes. You can press CLEAR to erase the expression and then enter a new expression.
	The expression is stored as one of the ten user-defined functions in the Y= list as you enter it.
Clearing a Function	To clear or erase a function on the Y= edit screen, position the cursor anywhere on the function, and then press CLEAR.
Defining Functions from the Home Screen or a Program	1. Begin on a blank line. Press ALPHA ["], enter the expression, and then press ALPHA ["] again.
	2. Press STO▶.
	3. Press 2nd [Y-VARS], select **Function...**, and then select the name of the function, which is copied to the cursor location.
	4. Press ENTER to complete the instruction.
	"expression"➔**Y***n*
	When the instruction is executed, the TI-82 stores the expression to the Y= list, selects the function, and displays the message Done.
Evaluating Y= Functions in Expressions	You can the calculate the value of a Y= function at a specified value of **X**. For example, if **Y₁=.2X³–2X+6**:

```
Y₁(0)
                      6
Y₁({0,1,2,3,4})
{6 4.2 3.6 5.4 …
```

Selecting Functions

Only functions that are selected are graphed. Up to ten functions may be selected at one time.

Turning a Function "On" or "Off"	You select and deselect ("turn on" and "turn off") functions on the Y= edit screen. The = sign on a selected function is highlighted. To change the selection status of a function:

1. If the Y= edit screen is not displayed, press Y= to display the functions.

2. Move the cursor to the function whose status you want to change.

3. Use ◄ to place the cursor over the = sign of the function.

4. Press ENTER to change the status.

Note: When you enter or edit a function, it is selected automatically. When you clear a function, it is deselected.

Leaving the Y= Edit Screen	To leave the Y= edit screen:

• Select another screen by pressing the appropriate key, such as GRAPH or WINDOW.

• Press 2nd [QUIT] to return to the Home screen.

Selecting Functions from the Home Screen or a Program	1. Begin on a blank line. Press 2nd [Y-VARS] and select **On/Off...** . The ON/OFF menu is displayed.

2. Select the instruction you want, **FnOn** or **FnOff**. It is copied to the cursor location.

3. If you want to turn specific functions on or off, enter the number of the function(s), separated by commas.

When the instruction is executed, the status of each function in the current graph mode is set appropriately and Done is displayed.

FnOn
FnOff
FnOn *function1,function2,* . . .
FnOff *function1,function2,* . . .

For example, in **Func** MODE, **FnOff:FnOn 1,3** turns off all functions in the Y= list and then turns on **Y1** and **Y3**.

Defining the Viewing WINDOW

The WINDOW variables determine the boundaries and other attributes of the viewing WINDOW. The WINDOW variables are shared by all graphing modes.

TI-82 Viewing WINDOW

The viewing WINDOW of the TI-82 is the portion of the coordinate plane defined by **Xmin**, **Xmax**, **Ymin**, and **Ymax**. The distance between tick marks is defined by **Xscl** for the **X** axis and **Yscl** for the **Y** axis.

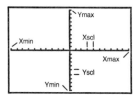

Checking the Viewing WINDOW

Press WINDOW to display the current WINDOW variable values. The values shown here are the standard values.

```
WINDOW FORMAT
 Xmin=-10
 Xmax=10
 Xscl=1
 Ymin=-10
 Ymax=10
 Yscl=1
```

Changing a WINDOW Variable Value

1. Press ▼ to move to the WINDOW variable you want to change.

2. To enter a real value (which can be an expression), you may do any of the following:

   • Position the cursor and then make the changes.

   • Press CLEAR to clear the value and then enter a new value.

   • Begin entering a new value. The original value is cleared automatically when you begin typing.

3. Press ENTER, ▼, or ▲. If you entered an expression, it is evaluated. The new value is stored.

Xmin must be less than **Xmax** and **Ymin** must be less than **Ymax**, or you will get an error message when you press GRAPH. To turn off the tick marks, set **Xscl=0** or **Yscl=0**.

Leaving the WINDOW Edit Screen	To leave the WINDOW edit screen:

- Select another screen by pressing the appropriate key, such as ⌊GRAPH⌋ or ⌊Y=⌋.

- Press ⌊2nd⌋ [QUIT] to return to the Home screen.

Storing to a WINDOW Variable from the Home Screen or a Program

Begin on a blank line.

1. Enter the value you want to store (which can be an expression).

2. Press ⌊STO▶⌋.

3. Press ⌊VARS⌋ to display the VARS menu.

4. Select **Window...** to display the WINDOW variables.

5. Select the WINDOW variable to which you want to store. The name of the variable is copied to the cursor location where you are editing.

6. Press ⌊ENTER⌋ to complete the instruction.

When the instruction is executed, the TI-82 stores the value in the WINDOW variable.

Note: You can use a WINDOW variable in an expression by performing steps 3, 4, and 5.

ΔX and ΔY

The variables ΔX and ΔY define the distance between the centers of two adjoining pixels on a graph (graphing accuracy).

$$\Delta X = \frac{(Xmax - Xmin)}{94} \qquad \Delta Y = \frac{(Ymax - Ymin)}{62}$$

ΔX and ΔY are not on the WINDOW screen; they are accessible through the VARS Window menu. ΔX and ΔY are calculated from **Xmin**, **Xmax**, **Ymin**, and **Ymax** when a graph is displayed.

You can store values directly to ΔX and ΔY, in which case **Xmax** and **Ymax** are calculated from ΔX, **Xmin**, ΔY, and **Ymin** immediately.

Setting WINDOW FORMAT

WINDOW FORMAT determines how a graph appears on the display. WINDOW FORMAT settings apply to all graphing modes.

Checking WINDOW FORMAT

To display the WINDOW FORMAT screen, press WINDOW ▶. The current settings are highlighted.

```
WINDOW FORMAT
RectGC  PolarGC        Sets rectangular or polar cursor
CoordOn CoordOff       Sets cursor coordinates on or off
GridOff GridOn         Sets grid off or on
AxesOn  AxesOff        Sets axes on or off
LabelOff LabelOn       Sets axes label off or on
```

Changing WINDOW FORMAT

1. Move the cursor to the row of the setting you want to change. The setting the cursor is on blinks.

2. Move the cursor to the setting you want and press ENTER.

RectGC PolarGC

The cursor coordinate setting determines if the cursor location is displayed (if **CoordOn**) as rectangular coordinates **X** and **Y** or polar coordinates **R** and θ. It also determines which variables are updated. In **RectGC** (rectangular graphing coordinates) FORMAT, plotting the graph, moving the free-moving cursor, or tracing updates and displays **X** and **Y**. In **PolarGC** (polar graphing coordinates) FORMAT, **X, Y, R**, and θ are updated, and **R** and θ are displayed.

CoordOn CoordOff

CoordOn (coordinates on) displays the function number in the upper-right corner and the cursor coordinates at the bottom of the graph. **CoordOff** (coordinate off) does not display the function number or the coordinates for the free-moving cursor or during TRACE.

GridOff GridOn

Grid points correspond to the axis tick marks. **GridOff** does not display grid points. **GridOn** does display the grid points.

AxesOn AxesOff

AxesOn displays the axes. **AxesOff** does not display the axes. It overrides the Axis Label setting.

LabelOff LabelOn

LabelOn and **LabelOff** determine whether to display a label for the axes (**X** and **Y**).

Displaying a Graph

Pressing [GRAPH] graphs any functions selected on the Y=
edit screen. The current MODE settings apply, and the
current values of the WINDOW variables define the
viewing WINDOW.

**Displaying a
New Graph**

Press [GRAPH] to display the graph of the selected function
or functions. (Some operations, such as TRACE and the
ZOOM CALC operations, display the graph automatically.)
As a graph is plotted, the busy indicator is on and **X** and **Y**
are updated.

**Pausing a
Graph**

Note: While a graph is being plotted, you can:

• Press [ENTER] to pause graphing, then press [ENTER] to
  resume plotting.

• Press [ON] to stop graphing, then press [GRAPH] to start
  over.

Smart Graph

When you press [GRAPH], Smart Graph displays the graph
screen immediately if nothing has changed that requires
the functions to be replotted since the last time the graph
was displayed.

If you have not changed any of the following since the
graph was last displayed, Smart Graph displays the graph
immediately. If you have changed one or more of these,
pressing [GRAPH] replots the graph based on the new values.

• Changed a MODE setting that affects graphs.

• Changed a function.

• Selected or deselected a function.

• Changed the value of a variable in a selected function.

• Changed a WINDOW variable or a FORMAT setting.

• Cleared drawings by selecting **ClrDraw** (Chapter 8).

• Changed a STAT PLOT definition (Chapter 12).

Displaying a Graph (Continued)

Graphing a Family of Curves

If you enter a list (Chapter 11) as an element in an expression, the TI-82 plots the function for each value in the list, graphing a family of curves. (In **Simul**, it graphs all functions for the first element, and so on.)

{2,4,6}sin X graphs three functions: **2 sin X**, **4 sin X**, and **6 sin X**.

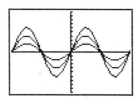

{2,4,6}sin {1,2,3}X graphs **2 sin X**, **4 sin 2X**, and **6 sin 3X**.

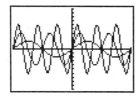

Exploring a Graph with the Free-Moving Cursor

While a graph is displayed, you can move the free-moving cursor anywhere on the graph and display the coordinates of any location on the graph.

Free-Moving Cursor

You can use ◀, ▶, ▲, or ▼ to move the cursor around the graph. When you first display the graph, no cursor is visible. As soon as you press ◀, ▶, ▲, or ▼, the cursor moves from the center of the viewing window.

As you move the cursor around the graph, the coordinate values of the cursor location are displayed at the bottom of the screen (if **CoordOn**). Coordinate values generally appear in normal floating-decimal format. The numeric display settings on the MODE screen do not affect coordinate display.

To see the graph without the cursor or coordinate values, press CLEAR or ENTER. When you press ◀, ▶, ▲, or ▼, the cursor moves from same position.

Graphing Accuracy

The free-moving cursor moves from dot to dot on the screen. When you move the cursor to a dot that appears to be "on" the function, it may be near, but not on, the function; therefore, the coordinate value displayed at the bottom of the screen is not necessarily a point on the function. To move the cursor along a function, use TRACE (page 3-14).

The display coordinate values of the free-moving cursor approximate actual math coordinates accurate to within the width/height of the dot. As **Xmin** and **Xmax** (and **Ymin** and **Ymax**) get closer together (after a **Zoom In**, for example), graphing accuracy increases, and the coordinate values more closely approximate the math coordinates.

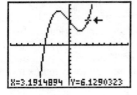

X=3.1914894   Y=6.1290323

◆ Free-moving cursor "on" the curve

Exploring a Graph with TRACE

TRACE moves the cursor from one plotted point to the
next along a function, while displaying the cursor
coordinates at the bottom of the screen.

**Beginning a
Trace**

Press [TRACE] to begin a trace. If the graph is not displayed
already, the TI-82 displays it. The cursor is on the first
selected function in the Y= list at the middle **X** value on the
screen. The number of the function shows at the upper
right of the display.

**Moving along a
Function**

[▶] and [◀] move the cursor along the function. Each press
moves the cursor from one plotted point to the next.
[2nd] [▶] and [2nd] [◀] move the cursor five plotted points at a
time. The **Y** value is calculated from the **X** value; that is,
Y=**Y**n(**X**). If the function is undefined at an **X** value, the **Y**
value is blank.

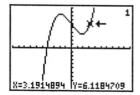

◀ TRACE cursor on the
curve.

If the **Y** value of a function is above or below the viewing
window, the cursor disappears as you move it to that
portion of the function; however, the coordinate values at
the bottom of the screen indicate the cursor coordinates.

**Panning to the
Left or Right**

If you trace a function off the left or right edge of the
screen, the viewing window automatically pans to the left
or right. **Xmin** and **Xmax** are updated to correspond to the
new viewing window.

QuickZoom

While tracing, you can press [ENTER] to adjust the viewing
WINDOW so that the cursor location becomes the center
of the new viewing WINDOW, even if the cursor is above or
below the display. This allows "panning" up and down.
After QuickZoom, the cursor remains in TRACE.

Moving from Function to Function

To trace another selected function on the graph, use ⌄ or ⌃ to move the cursor to that function. The cursor movement is based on the order of the selected functions in the Y= list, not the appearance of the functions as graphed on the screen. The cursor moves to the new function at the same **X** value. The function number in the upper right corner of the display changes.

Leaving TRACE

To leave TRACE:

- Select another screen by pressing the appropriate key, such as WINDOW or ZOOM.

- Press 2nd [QUIT] to return to the Home screen.

The TRACE cursor remains in the same location if you leave TRACE and return, if Smart Graph has not caused the graph to be replotted.

Using TRACE in a Program

On a blank line in the program editor, press TRACE. The instruction **Trace** is copied to the cursor location. When the instruction is encountered during program execution, the graph is displayed with the TRACE cursor on the first selected function. As you trace, the cursor coordinate values are updated. When you are done tracing functions, press ENTER to resume program execution.

Exploring a Graph with ZOOM

Pressing ZOOM accesses a menu that allows you to adjust the viewing WINDOW of the graph quickly in a variety of ways. All of the ZOOM commands are accessible from programs.

ZOOM Menu

```
ZOOM MEMORY
1:ZBox        Draws box to define viewing WINDOW
2:Zoom In     Magnifies graph around cursor
3:Zoom Out    Views more of graph around cursor
4:ZDecimal    Sets .1 as dot size
5:ZSquare     Sets equal sized dots on X and Y axes
6:ZStandard   Sets standard WINDOW variables
7:ZTrig       Sets built-in trig WINDOW variables
8:ZInteger    Sets integer values on X and Y axes
9:ZoomStat    Sets values for current lists
```

ZBox

ZBox lets you use the cursor to select opposite corners of a box to define a new viewing WINDOW.

1. Select **ZBox** from the ZOOM menu. The different cursor at the center of the screen indicates that you are using a ZOOM instruction.

2. Move the cursor to any corner of the box you want to define and then press ENTER. As you move the cursor away from the point just selected, you see a small square dot, indicating that the first corner is selected.

3. Move the cursor to the diagonal corner of the box you want to define. As you move the cursor, the boundaries of the box change on the screen.

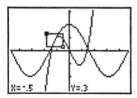

Note: You can cancel **ZBox** any time before you press ENTER by pressing CLEAR.

4. When the box is defined as you want it, press ENTER to replot the graph.

You can repeat steps 2 through 4 to do another **ZBox**. To cancel **ZBox**, press CLEAR.

Zoom In
Zoom Out

Zoom In magnifies the graph around the cursor location.
Zoom Out displays a greater portion of the graph, centered
on the cursor location, to provide a more global view. The
XFact and **YFact** settings determine the extent of the
zoom.

1. After checking or changing **XFact** and **YFact**
   (page 3-20), select **Zoom In** from the ZOOM menu.

   Notice the different cursor. It indicates that you are
   using a ZOOM instruction.

2. Move the cursor to the point that you want as the
   center of the new viewing WINDOW, then press ENTER.

   The TI-82 adjusts the viewing WINDOW by **XFact** and
   YFact, updates the WINDOW variables, and replots the
   selected functions, centered on the cursor location.

3. To zoom in on the graph again:

   • To zoom in at the same point, press ENTER.

   • To zoom in at a new point, move the cursor to the
     point that you want as the center of the new
     viewing WINDOW and then press ENTER.

Zoom Out

The procedure for **Zoom Out** is the same as for **Zoom In**.

Leaving Zoom
In or Zoom Out

To leave **Zoom In** or **Zoom Out**:

   • Select another screen by pressing the appropriate key,
     such as TRACE or GRAPH.

   • Press 2nd [QUIT] to return to the Home screen.

Exploring a Graph with ZOOM (Continued)

ZDecimal   **ZDecimal** replots the functions immediately, updating the WINDOW variables to preset values that set ΔX and ΔY equal to **.1** and defining the **X** and **Y** value of each pixel as one decimal.

Xmin = -4.7   Ymin = -3.1
Xmax = 4.7   Ymax = 3.1
Xscl = 1   Yscl = 1

ZSquare   **ZSquare** replots the functions immediately, redefining the WINDOW based on the current WINDOW variables, but adjusted in only one direction so that ΔX=ΔY. This makes the graph of a circle look like a circle. **Xscl** and **Yscl** remain unchanged. The midpoint of the current graph (not the intersection of the axes) becomes the midpoint of the new graph.

ZStandard ZStandard replots the functions immediately, updating the WINDOW variables to the standard values:

Xmin = -10   Ymin = -10
Xmax = 10   Ymax = 10
Xscl = 1   Yscl = 1

ZTrig   **ZTrig** replots the functions immediately, updating the WINDOW variables to preset values appropriate for trig plotting functions. In **Radian** MODE these are:

Xmin = -(47/24)π   Ymin = -3
Xmax = (47/24)π   Ymax = 3
Xscl = π/2   Yscl = 1

ZInteger   **ZInteger** redefines the viewing WINDOW so ΔX=1 and ΔY=1, **Xscl**=10, and **Yscl** = 10, replotting the functions after you move the cursor to the point that you want as the center of the new WINDOW and press ENTER.

ZoomStat   **ZoomStat** redefines the viewing WINDOW so that all statistical data points are displayed. For one-variable plots (histograms and box plots), only **Xmin** and **Xmax** are adjusted. If the top of the histogram is not shown, use TRACE to determine the value for **Ymax**.

Using ZOOM MEMORY

ZPrevious allows you to return to the WINDOW displayed prior to the previous ZOOM. ZoomSto stores the values of the current WINDOW variables to user-defined ZOOM MEMORY variables. ZoomRcl changes the WINDOW to the values stored with ZoomSto.

ZOOM MEMORY Menu

```
ZOOM MEMORY
1:ZPrevious      Uses previous viewing WINDOW
2:ZoomSto        Stores user-defined WINDOW
3:ZoomRcl        Recalls user-defined WINDOW
4:SetFactors...  Changes Zoom In, Zoom Out factors
```

ZPrevious

When you select **ZPrevious** from the ZOOM MEMORY menu, the graph is replotted using the WINDOW variables of the graph displayed prior to the previous ZOOM that you did.

ZoomSto

To store the current viewing WINDOW, select **ZoomSto** from the ZOOM MEMORY menu. The graph is displayed if necessary, and the values of the current WINDOW variables are stored in the user-defined ZOOM variables: **ZXmin**, **ZXmax**, **ZXscl**, **ZYmin**, **ZYmax**, and **ZYscl**. The action is immediate, there is no prompting on the display.

These variables are global; they apply to all graphing modes. For example, changing the value of **ZXmin** in **Func** MODE also changes it in **Par** MODE.

The user-defined WINDOW variables contain the standard values until you store to them the first time.

ZoomRcl

To view the selected graphing functions in the user-defined WINDOW, select **ZoomRcl** from the ZOOM MEMORY menu. The WINDOW variables are updated with the user-defined values, and the graph is plotted.

Using ZOOM MEMORY from the Home Screen or a Program

From the Home screen or a program, you can store directly to any of the user-defined ZOOM variables.

From a program, you can select the **ZoomSto** or **ZoomRcl** instructions from the ZOOM MEMORY menu.

Setting ZOOM FACTORS

The ZOOM FACTORS, XFact and YFact, determine the extent of the change for the viewing window created by Zoom In or Zoom Out on a graph.

ZOOM FACTORS

ZOOM FACTORS are positive numbers (not necessarily integers) greater than or equal to 1. They define the magnification or reduction factor used to **Zoom In** or **Zoom Out** around a point.

Checking XFact and YFact

To review the current values of **XFact** and **YFact**, select **SetFactors...** from the ZOOM MEMORY menu. The ZOOM FACTORS screen appears (the values shown are the standard values).

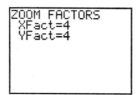

Changing XFact and YFact

To change **XFact** or **YFact**:

• Enter a new value. The original value is cleared automatically when you begin typing.

• Position the cursor over the digit you want to change. Then type over it or use DEL to delete it.

Leaving ZOOM FACTORS

To leave ZOOM FACTORS:

• Select another screen by pressing the appropriate key, such as WINDOW or ZOOM.

• Press 2nd [QUIT] to return to the Home screen.

Using CALC (Calculate) Operations

Pressing [2nd] [CALC] (above [TRACE]) accesses a menu with operations you can use to analyze the current graph functions. You are prompted to specify the function(s), interval, and point.

CALCULATE Menu

CALCULATE	
1:value	Calculates function value for given **X**
2:root	Finds root of function
3:minimum	Finds minimum of function
4:maximum	Finds maximum of function
5:intersect	Finds intersection of functions
6:dy/dx	Finds numeric derivative of function
7:∫f(x)dx	Finds numeric integral of function

value

value evaluates currently selected functions for a specified value of **X**.

1. Select **value** from the CALC menu. The current graph is displayed, with a prompt for you to enter **X**.

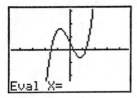

2. Enter a real value for **X** between **Xmin** and **Xmax** (which can be an expression). **Note:** When there is a value entered for **X**, [CLEAR] clears the value; when there is no value, [CLEAR] cancels **value**.

3. Press [ENTER]. The result cursor is on the first selected function in the list at the entered **X** and the coordinate values are displayed (even if you have selected **CoordOff** on the WINDOW FORMAT screen).

4. Press ⬇ or ⬆ to move the cursor between functions at the entered **X** value. When ◀ or ▶ are pressed, the free-moving cursor appears. It cannot necessarily move back to the **X** value.

root

root (CALC item 2) uses **solve(** (Chapter 2) to find the root (zero or **X**-intercept) of a function to a tolerance of 1E-5. Selecting good values for the bounds and a guess help it find the correct root and find it more quickly.

1. Select **root** from the CALC menu. The current graph is displayed, with a prompt to enter Lower Bound.

2. Use ▼ or ▲ to move the cursor to the function for which you want to find the root.

3. Move the cursor to the **X** value you want for the lower bound of the interval and press ENTER. A ▶ indicator at the top of the display shows the lower bound.

4. Set the upper bound in the same way. An indicator shows the upper bound.

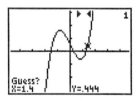

5. You are prompted for a Guess to help the TI-82 find the correct root and to find it more quickly.

6. Use ◀ or ▶ to move the cursor to a point near the root of the function, between the bounds. Press ENTER.

The result cursor is on the solution and the coordinate values are displayed (even if you have selected **CoordOff** on the WINDOW FORMAT screen). When you press ◀, ▶, ▲, or ▼, the free-moving cursor appears.

minimum	minimum (CALC item 3) and maximum (CALC item 4) find
maximum	the minimum or maximum of a function in a specified
	interval to a tolerance of 1E-5.

1. Select **minimum** or **maximum** from the CALC menu. The current graph is displayed.

2. Set Lower Bound, Upper Bound, and Guess as described for **root**.

The result cursor is on the solution and the coordinate values are displayed (even if you have selected **CoordOff** on the WINDOW FORMAT screen). When you press ◁, ▷, ▲, or ▼, the free-moving cursor appears.

intersect intersect (CALC item 5) finds the intersection of two functions to a tolerance of 1E-5. The intersection must appear on the display.

1. Select **intersection** from the CALC menu. The current graph is displayed and you are prompted to select the First curve.

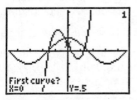

2. Use ▼ or ▲ to move the cursor to the first function and press [ENTER].

3. Use ▼ or ▲ to move the cursor to the second function and press [ENTER].

The result cursor is on the solution and the coordinate values are displayed (even if you have selected **CoordOff** on the WINDOW FORMAT screen). When you press ◁, ▷, ▲, or ▼, the free-moving cursor appears.

Using CALC (Calculate) Operations (Continued)

dy/dx

dy/dx (numerical derivative, CALC item 6) finds the numerical derivative (slope) of a function at a point with ε = 1E-3.

1. Select **dy/dx** from the CALC menu. The current graph is displayed.

2. Move the cursor to the **X** value at which you want to calculate the derivative and press [ENTER].

The result cursor is on the solution and the coordinate values are displayed (even if you have selected **CoordOff** on the WINDOW FORMAT screen). When you press ◁, ▷, ▲, or ▼, the free-moving cursor appears.

∫f(x)dx

∫f(x)dx (numerical integral, CALC item 7) finds the numerical integral of a function in a specified interval. It uses the **fnInt(** function, with a tolerance of 1E-3.

1. Select **∫f(x)dx** from the CALC menu. The current graph is displayed, with a prompt to enter Lower Bound.

2. Use ▼ or ▲ to move the cursor to the function for which you want to calculate the integral.

3. Set Lower Limit and Upper Limit as described for **root**.

The integral value is displayed and the integrated area is shaded. When you press ◁, ▷, ▲, or ▼, the free-moving cursor appears.

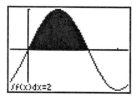

Note: The shaded area is a drawing. Use **ClrDraw** or any change that invokes Smart Graph to clear the shaded area. (Chapter 8).

Chapter 4: Parametric Graphing

This chapter describes how to graph parametric equations on the TI-82. Before doing parametric graphing, you should be familiar with Chapter 3, Function Graphing.

Chapter Contents

Getting Started: Path of a Ball

Getting Started is a fast-paced introduction. Read the chapter for details.

Graph the parametric equation that describes the position of a ball kicked at an angle of 60° with an initial velocity of 15 meters per second. (Ignore air resistance.) What is the maximum height? When does the ball strike the ground?

1. Press [MODE]. Press ▼ ▼ ▼ ▶ [ENTER] to select **Par** MODE.

    For initial velocity v_0 and angle θ, the horizontal component of the position of the ball as a function of time is $X(t) = tv_0\cos\theta$. The vertical component is $Y(t) = tv_0\sin\theta - (g/2)t^2$. The gravity constant g is 9.8 m/sec^2.

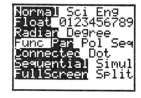

2. Press [Y=]. Press **15** [X,T,Θ] [COS] **60** [2nd] [ANGLE] **1** (to select °) [ENTER] to define the **X** portion of the parametric equation in terms of **T**.

3. Press **15** [X,T,Θ] [SIN] **60** [2nd] [ANGLE] **1** (to select °) [-] [(] **9.8** [÷] **2** [)] [X,T,Θ] [x²] [ENTER] to define the **Y** portion.

4. Press [WINDOW]. Press ▼ to move to **Tmin** and then enter the WINDOW variables appropriate for this problem.

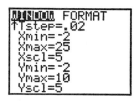

Tmin=0	Xmin=-2	Ymin=-2
Tmax=3	Xmax=25	Ymax=10
Tstep=.02	Xscl=5	Yscl=5

5. Press [TRACE] to graph the position of the ball as a function of time.

    Tracing begins at **Tmin**. As you press ▶ to trace the curve, the cursor follows the path of the ball over time. The values for **X** (distance), **Y** (height), and **T** (time) are displayed at the bottom of the screen.

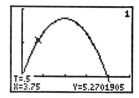

Defining and Displaying a Parametric Graph

Parametric equations consist of an X component and a Y component, each expressed in terms of the same independent variable T. They are often used to graph equations over time. Up to six pairs of parametric equations can be defined and graphed at a time.

Defining a Parametric Graph

The steps for defining a parametric graph are the same as those for defining a function graph. Differences are noted below.

Setting Parametric Graph Modes

Press MODE to display the MODE settings. To graph parametric equations, you must select **Par** before you enter WINDOW variables or enter the components of parametric equations. Also, you usually should select **Connected** to obtain a more meaningful **Par** graph.

Displaying Parametric Equations

After selecting **Par** MODE, press Y= to display the parametric Y= edit screen.

```
X₁ᴛ =■
Y₁ᴛ =
X₂ᴛ =
Y₂ᴛ =
X₃ᴛ =
Y₃ᴛ =
X₄ᴛ =
Y₄ᴛ =
```

On this screen, you display and enter both **X** and **Y** components. TI-82 has six equations, each defined in terms of **T**.

Defining Parametric Equations

Follow the same procedures as for **Func** graphing to enter the two components that define a new parametric equation.

• You must define both the **X** and **Y** components in a pair.

• The independent variable in each component is **T**. You may press X,T,Θ, rather than pressing ALPHA [T], to enter the parametric variable **T**. (**Par** MODE defines the independent variable as **T**.)

Defining and Displaying Parametric Equations (Cont.)

Selecting Parametric Equations

Only the selected parametric equations are graphed. The = sign on both components of selected equations is highlighted. You may select any or all of the equations on the parametric Y= edit screen.

To change the selection status of a parametric equation, press [◄] to move the cursor onto the = sign on either the **X** or **Y** component and press [ENTER]. The status on both the **X** and **Y** components is changed.

Note: When you enter both components of an equation or edit either component, that equation is selected automatically.

Setting WINDOW Variables

Press [WINDOW] to display the current WINDOW variable values. The WINDOW variables define the viewing WINDOW. The values shown are the standard values in **Radian** MODE.

Tmin=0	Smallest **T** value to evaluate
Tmax=6.2831853...	Largest **T** value to evaluate (2π)
Tstep=.1308996...	**T** value increment ($\pi/24$)
Xmin=-10	Smallest **X** value to be displayed
Xmax=10	Largest **X** value to be displayed
Xscl=1	Spacing between **X** tick marks
Ymin=-10	Smallest **Y** value to be displayed
Ymax=10	Largest **Y** value to be displayed
Yscl=1	Spacing between **Y** tick marks

You may want to change the **T** WINDOW variable values to ensure that sufficient points are plotted.

Setting the WINDOW FORMAT

Press [WINDOW] [▶] to display the current WINDOW FORMAT settings. The formats are shared with the other graphing modes.

Displaying a Graph

When you press [GRAPH], the TI-82 plots the selected parametric equations. It evaluates both the **X** and the **Y** component for each value of **T** (from **Tmin** to **Tmax** in intervals of **Tstep**) and then plots each point defined by **X** and **Y**. The WINDOW variables define the viewing WINDOW.

As a graph is plotted, the TI-82 updates **X**, **Y**, and **T**.

Smart Graph applies to parametric graphs.

WINDOW Variables and Y-VARS Menus

From the Home screen, you can:

*   Access functions by using the name of the component of the equation as a variable.

*   Select or deselect parametric equations from a program.

*   Store parametric equations.

*   Store values directly to WINDOW variables.

Exploring a Parametric Graph

As in Function graphing, three tools are available for exploring a graph: using the free-moving cursor, tracing an equation, and zooming.

Free-Moving Cursor

The free-moving cursor works in **Par** graphing just as it does in **Func** graphing. In **RectGC** FORMAT, moving the cursor updates and displays (if FORMAT is **CoordOn**) the values of **X** and **Y**. (In **PolarGC** FORMAT, **X**, **Y**, **R**, and θ are updated, and **R** and θ are displayed.)

TRACE

TRACE lets you move the cursor along the equation one **Tstep** at a time. When you begin a trace, the cursor is on the first selected equation at **Tmin**. The number of the equation shows in the upper right of the display.

In **RectGC** FORMAT, TRACE updates and displays (if FORMAT is **CoordOn**) the values of **X**, **Y**, and **T**. (In **PolarGC** FORMAT, **X**, **Y**, **R**, θ and **T** are updated, and **R**, θ, and **T** are displayed.) The **X** and **Y** (or **R** and θ) values are calculated from **T**.

If the cursor moves off the top or bottom of the screen, the coordinate values at the bottom of the screen continue to change appropriately.

[2nd] [◄] and [2nd] [►] move the TRACE cursor five plotted points at a time. The TRACE cursor remains in the same location if you leave TRACE and return, if Smart Graph has not caused the graph to be replotted.

QuickZoom is available in **Par** graphing, but panning is not.

ZOOM

ZOOM operations work in **Par** graphing as they do in **Func** graphing. Only the **X** (**Xmin**, **Xmax**, and **Xscl**) and **Y** (**Ymin**, **Ymax**, and **Yscl**) WINDOW variables are affected. **T** WINDOW variables (**Tmin**, **Tmax**, and **Tstep**) are not affected, except when you select **ZStandard** (**Tmin** = 0, **Tmax** = 2π, and **Tstep** = $\pi/24$). ZOOM MEMORY variables in **Par** graphing include **ZTmin**, **ZTmax**, and **ZTstep**.

CALC

CALC operations work in **Par** graphing as they do in **Func** graphing. CALC operations available in **Par** graphing are **value**, **dy/dx**, **dy/dt**, and **dx/dt**.

Chapter 5: Polar Graphing

This chapter describes how to graph polar equations on the TI-82. Before doing polar graphing, you should be familiar with Chapter 3, Function Graphing.

Chapter Contents

Getting Started: Polar Rose

Getting Started is a fast-paced introduction. Read the chapter for details.

The polar equation A sin Bθ graphs a rose. Graph the rose for A=8 and B=2.5, then explore the appearance of the rose for other values of A and B.

1. Press $\boxed{\text{MODE}}$. Press $\boxed{\blacktriangledown}$ $\boxed{\blacktriangledown}$ $\boxed{\blacktriangledown}$ $\boxed{\blacktriangleright}$ $\boxed{\blacktriangleright}$ $\boxed{\text{ENTER}}$ to select **Pol** MODE. Choose the initial settings for the other modes (the choice at the beginning of each line).

2. Press $\boxed{\text{Y=}}$ to display the polar Y= edit screen. Press **8** $\boxed{\text{SIN}}$ **2.5** $\boxed{\text{X,T,Θ}}$ $\boxed{\text{ENTER}}$ to define **r1**.

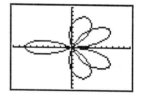

3. Press $\boxed{\text{ZOOM}}$ **6** to select **ZStandard** to graph the equation in the standard viewing WINDOW. Notice that the graph shows only five petals of the rose and that the rose does not appear symmetrical. This is because the standard WINDOW defines the WINDOW, rather than the pixels, as square and sets **θmax=2π**.

4. Press $\boxed{\text{WINDOW}}$ to display the WINDOW settings. Press $\boxed{\blacktriangledown}$ $\boxed{\blacktriangledown}$ **4** $\boxed{\text{2nd}}$ $\boxed{[\pi]}$ to increase the value of **θmax**.

5. Press $\boxed{\text{ZOOM}}$ **5** to select **ZSquare** and plot the graph.

6. Continue, changing **A** and **B** to other values.

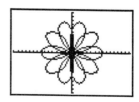

Defining and Displaying a Polar Graph

Polar equations are defined in terms of the independent variable θ. Up to six polar equations can be defined and graphed at a time.

Defining a Polar Graph

The steps for defining a polar graph are the same as those for defining a function graph. Differences are noted below.

Setting Polar Graph Modes

Press MODE to display the MODE settings. To graph polar equations, you must select **Pol** before you enter WINDOW variables or enter a polar equation. Also, you usually should select **Connected** to obtain a more meaningful **Pol** graph.

Displaying Polar Equations

After selecting **Pol** MODE, press Y= to display the polar Y= edit screen.

```
r1=█
r2=
r3=
r4=
r5=
r6=
```

On this screen, you display and enter polar equations. The TI-82 has six equations, each defined in terms of θ.

Defining Polar Equations

Follow the same procedures as for **Func** graphing to define a new polar equation. The independent variable in a polar equation is θ. You may press X,T,Θ, rather than pressing ALPHA [θ], to enter the polar variable θ. (**Pol** MODE defines the independent variable as θ.)

Selecting Polar Equations

Only the selected polar equations are graphed. The = sign on selected equations is highlighted. You may select any or all of the equations on the polar Y= edit screen.

To change the selection status of a polar equation, press ◄ to move the cursor onto the = sign and press ENTER.

Note: When you edit an equation, that equation is selected automatically.

Defining and Displaying a Polar Graph (Continued)

**Setting
WINDOW
Variables**

Press WINDOW to display the current WINDOW variable
values. The WINDOW variables define the viewing
WINDOW. The values shown are the standard values in
Radian MODE.

θmin=0	Smallest θ value to be evaluated
θmax=6.2831853...	Largest θ value to evaluate (2π)
θstep=.1308996...	Increment between θ values (π/24)
Xmin=-10	Smallest **X** value to be displayed
Xmax=10	Largest **X** value to be displayed
Xscl=1	Spacing between **X** tick marks
Ymin=-10	Smallest **Y** value to be displayed
Ymax=10	Largest **Y** value to be displayed
Yscl=1	Spacing between **Y** tick marks

You may want to change the θ WINDOW variable values to
ensure that sufficient points are plotted.

**Setting the
WINDOW
FORMAT**

Press WINDOW ▶ to display the current WINDOW FORMAT
settings. The formats are shared with the other graphing
modes.

Displaying a Graph

When you press GRAPH, the TI-82 plots the selected polar equations. It evaluates **R** for each value of θ (from θ**min** to θ**max** in intervals of θ**step**) and then plots each point.

As a graph is plotted, the TI-82 updates **X**, **Y**, **R**, and θ.

Smart Graph applies to polar graphs.

Note that the free-moving cursor displays **X** and **Y** coordinate values if the WINDOW FORMAT setting is the default **RectGC**. To see **R** and θ, select **PolarGC** WINDOW FORMAT.

WINDOW Variables and Y-VARS Menus

From the Home screen, you can:

• Access functions by using the name of the equation as a variable.

• Select or deselect polar equations from a program.

• Store polar equations.

• Store values directly to WINDOW variables.

Exploring a Polar Graph

As in function graphing, three tools are available for exploring a graph: using the free-moving cursor, tracing an equation, and zooming.

Free-Moving Cursor

The free-moving cursor works in **Pol** graphing just as it does in **Func** graphing. In **RectGC** FORMAT, moving the cursor updates and displays (if FORMAT is **CoordOn**) the values of **X** and **Y**. (In **PolarGC** FORMAT, **X**, **Y**, **R**, and θ are updated, and **R** and θ are displayed.)

TRACE

TRACE lets you move the cursor along the equation one θ**step** at a time. When you begin a trace, the cursor is on the first selected equation at θ**min**. The number of the equation shows in the upper right of the display.

In **RectGC** FORMAT, TRACE updates and displays (if FORMAT is **CoordOn**) the values of **X**, **Y**, and θ. (In **PolarGC** FORMAT, **X**, **Y**, **R**, and θ are updated, and **R** and θ are displayed.)

If the cursor moves off the top or bottom of the screen, the coordinate values at the bottom of the screen continue to change appropriately.

[2nd] [◄] and [2nd] [►] move the TRACE cursor five plotted points at a time. The TRACE cursor remains in the same location if you leave TRACE and return, if Smart Graph has not caused the graph to be replotted.

QuickZoom is available in **Pol** graphing, but panning is not.

ZOOM

ZOOM operations work in **Pol** graphing as they do in **Func** graphing. Only the **X** (**Xmin**, **Xmax**, and **Xscl**) and **Y** (**Ymin**, **Ymax**, and **Yscl**) WINDOW variables are affected. The θ WINDOW variables (θ**min**, θ**max**, and θ**step**) are not affected, except when you select **ZStandard** (θ**min** = 0, θ**max** = 2π, and θ**step** = $\pi/24$). The ZOOM MEMORY variables in **Pol** graphing include **Z**θ**min**, **Z**θ**max**, and **Z**θ**step**.

CALC

CALC operations work in **Pol** graphing as they do in **Func** graphing. The CALC operations available in **Pol** graphing are **value**, **dy/dx**, and **dr/d**θ.

Chapter 6: Sequence Graphing

This chapter describes how to graph sequences on the TI-82. Before doing sequence graphing, you should be familiar with Chapter 3, Function Graphing.

Chapter Contents

Getting Started: Forest and Trees

Getting Started is a fast-paced introduction. Read the chapter for details.

A small forest contains 4000 trees. The new forestry plan is that each year 20% of the trees will be harvested and 1000 new trees will be planted. Will the forest disappear? Does it stabilize at a certain number of trees? If so, what is that number?

---

1. Press [MODE]. Press ⊡ ⊡ ⊡ ▸ ▸ ▸ [ENTER] to select **Seq** MODE. Press ⊡ ▸ [ENTER] to select **Dot** MODE.

2. Press [Y=]. Each year the number of trees is 80 percent of what was there at the end of the prior year. Press [MATH] ▸ **2** (to select **iPart**, because the company will not harvest part of a tree) [(] **.8** [2nd] [Un-1] (2nd function of [7]) [)] to define the number of trees after each harvest. Press [+] **1000** to define the replacement trees.

3. Press [WINDOW]. Press ⊡ to move to **UnStart**. Press **4000** [ENTER] to define the number of trees at the beginning of the program.

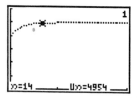

4. Press ⊡ ⊡ ⊡ **50** [ENTER] to set **nMax=50** to plot the size of the forest over 50 years.

5. Set the other WINDOW variables:

   Xmin=0   Ymin=0
   Xmax=50   Ymax=6000
   Xscl=10   Yscl=1000

6. Press [TRACE]. Tracing begins at **nMin** (before the forestry program began). Press ▸ to trace the values year-by-year. The values for **n** (year) and **Un** (trees) are displayed at the bottom of the screen. How many years does it take to stabilize the size of the forest?

Defining and Displaying a Sequence Graph

There are two sequence functions, U*n* and V*n*. Sequence functions can be defined in terms of the independent variable (*n*) or the prior item in the sequence function (U*n-1* or V*n-1*). They also can be defined in terms of the prior term in the other sequence function.

Defining a Sequence Graph

The basic steps for defining a sequence graph are the same as those for defining a function graph. Differences are noted below.

Setting Sequence Graph Modes

Press MODE to display the MODE settings. To graph sequence functions, you must select **Seq** before you enter WINDOW variables or enter the sequence functions. You may also want to select **Dot** to show discrete values more clearly. Note that sequence graphs automatically plot in **Simul** MODE, regardless of the current MODE setting.

Displaying Sequence Functions

After selecting **Seq** MODE, press Y= to display the sequence Y= edit screen.

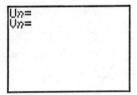

On this screen, you display and enter the sequence functions, U*n* and V*n*.

Defining Sequence Functions

Follow the same procedures as for **Func** graphing to enter the expression that defines a new sequence function. The *nth* term of U*n* or V*n* may be defined in one of two ways:

- Explicitly in terms of *n*; for example, U*n*=1/2^n. (*n* is the 2nd function of 9 on the keyboard, you cannot use X,T,Θ.)

- Recursively in terms of the prior element in a sequence using the variables U*n-1* and V*n-1* (the 2nd functions of 7 and 8); for example, U*n*=1/2^n can be entered as U*n*=(1/2)U*n-1* for U*n*Start=1.

Defining and Displaying Sequence Functions (Cont.)

Selecting Sequence Functions

Only the selected sequence functions are graphed. On selected functions the = sign is highlighted. You may select one or both of the functions on the sequence Y= edit screen.

To change the selection status of a sequence function, press [◄] to move the cursor onto the = sign and press [ENTER].

Note: When you enter or edit either function, that function is selected automatically.

Setting the WINDOW Variables

Press [WINDOW] to display the current WINDOW variable values. The WINDOW variables define the viewing WINDOW. The values shown are the standard defaults.

UnStart=0	Value of **Un** when **n=nStart**
VnStart=0	Value of **Vn** when **n=nStart**
nStart=0	Value of **n** at which calculation begins
nMin=0	Value of **n** at which plotting begins
nMax=10	Value of **n** at which plotting ends
Xmin=-10	Smallest **X** value to be displayed
Xmax=10	Largest **X** value to be displayed
Xscl=1	Spacing between **X** tick marks
Ymin=-10	Smallest **Y** value to be displayed
Ymax=10	Largest **Y** value to be displayed
Yscl=1	Spacing between **Y** tick marks

Note: If **Un** or **Vn** is nonrecursive (not defined in terms of **Un-1** or **Vn-1**), then **nMin** should not be **0** in **Time** FORMAT. **nMin** should usually equal **nStart** +1 to obtain a meaningful graph.

Setting WINDOW FORMAT	Press WINDOW ▶ to display the current WINDOW FORMAT settings. Sequence graphing has one unique format, **Time** or **Web**. The other formats are shared with the other graphing modes. **PolarGC** is ignored in **Time** FORMAT.

```
WINDOW FORMAT
Time    Web                Sets type of sequence plot
RectGC  PolarGC            Sets rectangular or polar cursor
CoordOn CoordOff           Sets cursor coordinate on or off
GridOff GridOn             Sets grid off or on
AxesOn  AxesOff            Sets axes on or off
LabelOff LabelOn           Sets axes label off or on
```

Displaying a Graph

As a **Seq** graph is plotted, the TI-82 updates **X**, **Y**, and **n**. Smart Graph applies to sequence graphs.

Time plots the sequence as a function of **n**. It evaluates **U**n and **V**n for each value of **n** (from **n**Min to **n**Max by **1**) and plots each point.

Web calculates **U**n as a function of **U**n-1 and **V**n as a function of **V**n-1. It plots **U**n-1 and **V**n-1 (independent variables) on the horizontal axis and **U**n and **V**n (dependent variables) on the vertical axis. The line **Y=X** is plotted automatically.

Evaluating Un **and V**n

From the Y-VARS menu, you can access the function names **U**n and **V**n to:

- Calculate the nth value in a sequence.
- Calculate a list of values in a sequence.
- Generate a sequence with **U**n(*nstart,nstop,nstep*). *nstep* is optional (if not specified, *nstep*=1).
  Note: **U**n and **V**n are invalid with **seq(**.

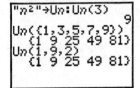

```
"n²"→Un:Un(3)
                9
Un({1,3,5,7,9})
    {1 9 25 49 81}
Un(1,9,2)
    {1 9 25 49 81}
```

Exploring a Sequence Graph

As in Function graphing, three tools are available for exploring a graph: using the free-moving cursor, tracing a function, and zooming.

Free-Moving Cursor

The free-moving cursor works in **Seq** graphing just as it does in **Func** graphing. In **RectGC** FORMAT, moving the cursor updates and displays (if FORMAT is **CoordOn**) the values of **X** and **Y**. (In **PolarGC Web** FORMAT, **X, Y, R**, and θ are updated, and **R** and θ are displayed.)

TRACE

In **Time** FORMAT, when you begin a trace, the cursor is on the first selected function at *n***Min**. TRACE displays (if FORMAT is **CoordOn**) the values of **U***n* or **V***n* and *n*. ▶ moves the cursor forward along the function one *n* at a time. It updates **U***n*, *n*, **X**, and **Y**.

In **Web** FORMAT, the trail left by the TRACE cursor helps identify points with attracting and repelling behavior in the sequence. When you begin a trace, the cursor is on the **X** axis at the value of **U***n***start** or **V***n***start** (the first selected function). TRACE displays and updates (if FORMAT is **CoordOn**) the values of *n*, **X**, and **Y** (or **R** and θ). **X** and **Y** (or **R** and θ) are calculated from *n*. ▶ moves the cursor between the function and the graph of **Y=X**, displaying both for *n* before incrementing *n*.

If the cursor moves off the top or bottom of the screen, the coordinate values at the bottom of the screen continue to change appropriately.

In **Seq**, ◀ or [2nd] ◀ moves the TRACE cursor to *n*=*n***Min**.

QuickZoom and panning are available in **Seq** graphing.

ZOOM

ZOOM operations works in **Seq** graphing as they do in **Func** graphing. Only the **X** (**Xmin, Xmax**, and **Xscl**) and **Y** (**Ymin, Ymax**, and **Yscl**) WINDOW variables are affected. **U***n***start, V***n***start, *n***Start, *n***Min**, and *n***Max** are not affected, except when you select **ZStandard** (**U***n***Start=0, V***n***Start=0, *n***Start=0, *n***Min=0** and *n***Max=10**). The ZOOM MEMORY variables in **Seq** graphing include **ZU***n***Start, ZV***n***Start, Z***n***Start, Z***n***Min**, and **Z***n***Max**.

CALC

value is the only CALC operation available in **Seq** graphing. It is not available in **Web** FORMAT.

Chapter 7: Tables

This chapter describes how to use tables on the TI-82.

Getting Started: Roots of a Function

Getting Started is a fast-paced introduction. Read the chapter for details.

Evaluate the function $Y=X^3-2X$ at each integer between -10 and 10. How many sign changes are there and where do they occur?

1. Press [2nd] [TblSet] to display the TABLE SETUP screen. Press [-] **10** to set **TblMin=-10**. Leave **ΔTbl=1**. Leave the independent and dependent value settings on **Auto**.

2. Press [Y=] [X,T,Θ] [MATH] **3** (to select **3**) [-] **2** [X,T,Θ] to enter the function **Y₁=X³-2X**.

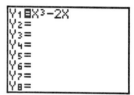

3. Press [2nd] [TABLE] to display the table screen.

X	Y₁	
-10	-980	
-9	-711	
-8	-496	
-7	-329	
-6	-204	
-5	-115	
-4	-56	
X=-10		

4. Press [▼] until you see the sign changes in the value of **Y₁**.

X	Y₁	
-3	-21	
-2	-4	
-1	1	
0	0	
1	-1	
2	4	
3	21	
X=3		

Defining the Variables

The independent variable for tables is the independent variable in the current graphing MODE. It is defined on the TABLE SETUP screen.

TABLE SETUP Screen

To display the TABLE SETUP screen, press [2nd] [TblSet].

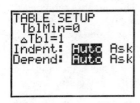

```
TABLE SETUP
 TblMin=0
 ⊿Tbl=1
Indpnt: Auto Ask
Depend: Auto Ask
```

TblMin and ⊿Tbl

TblMin (table minimum) applies when **Indpnt** is **Auto** (when the independent variable is automatically generated). It defines the initial value for the independent variable: **X** (**Func**), **T** (**Par**), θ (**Pol**), and *n* (**Seq**).

⊿Tbl (table step) defines the increment for the independent variable.

Note: In **Seq** MODE, **TblMin** and **⊿Tbl** both must be integers.

Indpnt: Auto or Ask

You can choose to display a table of values for the independent variable automatically or enter the values one at a time on the table. **Auto** generates and displays the values when the table is first displayed. **Ask** displays an empty table and you enter the values.

Depend: Auto or Ask

You can choose to display the values for the dependent variables automatically or one at a time. **Auto** calculates and displays all table values when the table is first displayed. **Ask** displays a table without values for the dependent variables. It calculates and displays a value for a specific location when you press [ENTER].

Setting Up a Table from the Home Screen or a Program

You can store values to **TblMin**, **⊿Tbl**, and **TblInput** from the Home screen or a program. The variable names are on the VARS TABLE menu. **TblInput** is a list of the values of the independent variable in the current table. In the program editor, when you press [2nd] [TblSet], you can select instructions for **IndpntAuto**, **IndpntAsk**, **DependAuto**, or **DependAsk**.

Defining the Dependent Variable

The selected Y*n* functions define the dependent
variables. You can have as many dependent variables as
there are functions in the current graphing MODE.

**From the Y=
Editor**

Enter the functions to define the dependent variables in
the Y= editor. The current graphing MODE is used. In **Par**,
you must define both components of the parametric
equation. Only functions that are selected are displayed in
the table (Chapter 3).

**From the Table
Editor**

Once a Y= function has been entered and selected, you can
change it from the table editor.

1. Move the cursor to the column of the dependent
   variable.

2. Press ▲ until the cursor is on the name of the function
   at the top of the column. The function is displayed on
   the bottom line.

3. You may edit the function. Press ENTER to switch to the
   editing context and make the changes. The function in
   the Y= table is updated.

4. Press ENTER or ▼. The new values are calculated, and
   the table is updated automatically.

Note: This feature also allows you to view the function
that defines the dependent variable(s) without leaving the
table.

Displaying the Table

The table displays two independent values for up to seven dependent values. Once the table is displayed, you can use ◄, ▲, ►, and ▼ to move around and scroll the table, displaying other independent variables and other dependent values.

The Table

Press [2nd] [TABLE] to display the table screen.

X	Y₁	Y₂
0	0	0
1	1	1
2	4	8
3	9	27
4	16	64
5	25	125
6	36	216

X=0

The top line displays the name of the independent variable and one or two dependent variables. The bottom line displays the full value of the current cell, as indicated by the rectangular cursor. The center portion is used to display the values, abbreviated if necessary, of the variables.

The selections you made on the TABLE SETUP screen determine which cells contain values when you press [2nd] [TABLE].

Indpnt: Auto **Depend: Auto**	Values appear in all cells in the table automatically.
Indpnt: Ask **Depend: Auto**	Table is empty. When a value is entered for the independent variable, the dependent values are calculated automatically.
Indpnt: Auto **Depend: Ask**	Values appear for the independent variable. To generate a value for a dependent variable, move to the specific cell and press [ENTER].
Indpnt: Ask **Depend: Ask**	Table is empty. Enter values for independent variable. To generate a value for a dependent variable, move to the specific cell and press [ENTER].

Displaying the Table (Continued)

Displaying More Independent Values

If you selected **Indpnt: Auto**, you can use ⬆ and ⬇ to display additional values of the independent variable and the corresponding dependent variables.

Note: You can scroll "back" from the value entered for **TblMin**. As you scroll, **TblMin** is updated automatically to the value shown on the top line of the table. For example, **TblMin=0** and **ΔTbl=1** generates and displays values of **X**=0, . . ., 6, but you can press ⬆ to scroll backwards and display the table for **X**=-1, . . ., 5.

X	Y₁	Y₂
-1	1	-1
0	0	0
1	1	1
2	4	8
3	9	27
4	16	64
5	25	125

X=-1

Displaying Other Dependent Variables

If you have more than two dependent variables defined, the first two in the Y= list are displayed. Press ▶ and ◀ to display other dependent variables.

X	Y₂	Y₃
-1	-1	1
0	0	0
1	1	1
2	8	16
3	27	81
4	64	256
5	125	625

Y₃=1

Clearing the Table

From a program, select the **ClrTable** instruction from the PRGM I/O menu. If TblSet is **IndpntAsk**, all independent variable values and dependent variable values on the table are cleared. If TblSet is **DependAsk**, all dependent variable values on the table are cleared.

Chapter 8: DRAW Operations

This chapter describes how to use the DRAW operations of the TI-82. Before using the DRAW operations, you should be familiar with Chapter 3, Function Graphing.

Chapter Contents

Getting Started: Shading a Graph

Getting Started is a fast-paced introduction. Read the chapter for details.

Shade the area above the function Y=X+1 and below the function Y=X³–8X.

1. Press [Y=] to see that all functions are deselected.

2. Press [ZOOM] **6** to reset the graph screen to the standard viewing WINDOW, clear any existing drawings, and display the viewing window.

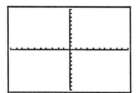

3. Press [2nd] [DRAW] and press **7** to select **Shade(**, which is copied to the Home screen.

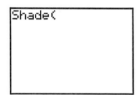

4. Press [X,T,Θ] [+] **1** [,] to define the function above which you want to shade.

5. Press [X,T,Θ] [MATH] **3** (to select ³) [–] **8** [X,T,Θ] [,] to define the function below which you want to shade.

6. Press **2** [)] to define the resolution for shading the graph.

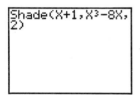

7. Press [ENTER] to execute the instruction. The two functions are drawn and the specified area shaded.

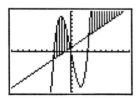

DRAW DRAW Menu

To display the DRAW DRAW menu, press [2nd] [DRAW]. What happens when you select an item from this menu is dependent on whether or not a graph is displayed when you access the menu, as described under each operation.

DRAW DRAW Menu

DRAW POINTS STO

1: ClrDraw	Clears all drawn elements
2: Line(	Draws a line between two points
3: Horizontal	Draws a horizontal line
4: Vertical	Draws a vertical line
5: Tangent(	Draws a line tangent to a function
6: DrawF	Draws a function
7: Shade(	Shades an area
8: DrawInv	Draws the inverse of a function
9: Circle(	Draws a circle
0: Text(	Annotates a graph with text
A: Pen	Free-form drawing tool

See page 8-16 for **ClrDraw**.

Before Drawing on a Graph

Because DRAW operations draw on top of the graph of currently selected functions, you may want to do one or more of the following before drawing on a graph:

- Change the MODE settings.

- Change the WINDOW FORMAT settings.

- Enter or edit functions in the Y= list.

- Select or deselect functions in the Y= list.

- Change WINDOW variable values.

- Turn Stat Plots on or off.

- Clear existing drawings with **ClrDraw** (page 8-16).

Drawing on a Graph

DRAW operations can draw on **Func**, **Par**, **Pol**, and **Seq** graphs, except **DrawInv**, which is valid only in **Func** graphing. The coordinates for all DRAW instructions are always the **X**-coordinate and **Y**-coordinate values of the display.

You can use most of the DRAW DRAW and DRAW POINTS operations to draw directly on a graph using the cursor to identify coordinates, or you can execute these instructions from the Home screen or a program. If a graph is not displayed when you select a DRAW operation, the Home screen is displayed automatically.

Drawing Lines

While a graph is displayed, Line(lets you define a line on the graph using the cursor. If a graph is not displayed, the instruction is copied to the Home screen.

Directly on a Graph

1. When a graph is displayed, select **Line(** from the DRAW DRAW menu (item 2).

2. Position the cursor at the beginning point of the line you want to draw. Press [ENTER].

3. Move the cursor to the end point of the line you want to draw. The line is displayed as you move the cursor. Press [ENTER].

To continue to draw lines, repeat steps 2 and 3. To cancel **Line(**, press [CLEAR].

From the Home Screen or a Program

Line((DRAW DRAW item 2) draws a line between the coordinates ($X1,Y1$) and ($X2,Y2$). The values may be entered as expressions.

Line($X1,Y1,X2,Y2$**)**

For example, **Line(0,0,6,9)** displays:

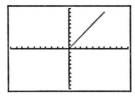

To erase a line:

Line($X1,Y1,X2,Y2$**,0)**

For example, **Line(2,3,4,6,0)** following the instruction above displays:

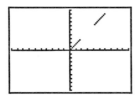

Drawing Horizontal and Vertical Lines

While a graph is displayed, Horizontal and Vertical let you define lines on the graph using the cursor. If a graph is not displayed, the instruction is copied to the Home screen.

Directly on a Graph

1. When a graph is displayed, select **Horizontal** (item 3) or **Vertical** (item 4) from the DRAW DRAW menu.

2. A line is displayed that moves as you move the cursor. Position the cursor where you want to draw the line. Press $\boxed{\text{ENTER}}$. The line is drawn on the graph.

To continue to draw lines, repeat step 2. To cancel **Horizontal** or **Vertical**, press $\boxed{\text{CLEAR}}$.

From the Home Screen or a Program

Horizontal (horizontal line) (DRAW DRAW item 3) draws a horizontal line at **Y**=Y (which can be an expression, but not a list).

Horizontal Y

Vertical (vertical line) (DRAW DRAW item 4) draws a vertical line at **X**=X (which can be an expression, but not a list).

Vertical X

For example, **Horizontal 7:Vertical 4:Vertical 5** displays:

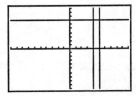

Drawing Tangent Lines

While a graph is displayed, you can draw the tangent line of a function at a specified point using the cursor. If a graph is not displayed, the instruction is copied to the Home screen.

Directly on a Graph

1. When a graph of selected functions is displayed, select **Tangent(** from the DRAW DRAW menu (item 5).

2. Use ⊟ and ⊡ to move the cursor to the function for which you want to draw the tangent line.

3. Use ⊡ and ⊡ to move the cursor to the point on the function at which you want to draw the tangent line.

4. Press [ENTER].

From the Home Screen or a Program

Tangent((tangent line) (DRAW DRAW item 5) draws a line tangent to an *expression* in terms of **X** (such as **Y₁** or **X²**) at point **X**=*value* (which can be an expression). *expression* is interpreted as being in **Func** MODE.

Tangent(*expression,value***)**

For example, if **Y₁**=**.2X³–2X+6** is the only selected function, **Tangent(Y₁,3)** plots **Y₁** and draws the tangent to the function at **X**=3:

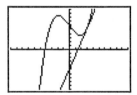

Drawing Functions and Inverses

DrawF (draw function) draws a function on the current graph. DrawInv (draw inverse) draws an inverse of a function on the current graph. Both instructions must be entered on the Home screen or in the program editor.

Drawing a Function

DrawF (draw function) (DRAW DRAW item 6) is not an interactive operation. It draws *expression* as a function in terms of **X** on the current graph.

DrawF *expression*

For example, if **Y₁=.2X³–2X+6** is the only selected function, **DrawF Y₁–5** plots **Y₁** and draws the function **Y₁–5**:

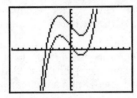

Note: A list cannot be used in *expression* to draw a family of curves.

Drawing an Inverse of a Function

DrawInv (draw inverse) (DRAW DRAW item 8) is not an interactive operation. It draws the inverse of an *expression* in terms of **X** on the current graph. You must be in **Func** MODE.

DrawInv *expression*

For example, if **Y₁=.2X³–2X+6** is the only selected function, **DrawInv Y₁** plots **Y₁** and draws its inverse:

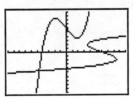

Shading Areas on a Graph

Shade(shades the area on a graph that is both below one specified function and above another, between two **X** values. The instruction must be entered on the Home screen or in the program editor.

Shading a Graph

Shade((DRAW DRAW item 7) is not an interactive operation. It draws *lowerfunc* and *upperfunc* in terms of **X** on the current graph and shades the area that is specifically above *lowerfunc* and below *upperfunc*. Only the areas where *lowerfunc* < *upperfunc* are shaded.

You can specify the shading *resolution* (an integer between 1 and 9). If none is specified, 1 is used. *resolution*=1 shades every pixel. *resolution*=2 shades every second pixel. *resolution*=3 shades every third pixel, and so on.

Optionally, you can specify *Xleft* (the left boundary) and *Xright* (the right boundary) for the shaded area. If *Xleft* or *Xright* are not specified, **Xmin** and **Xmax** are used.

Shade((*lowerfunc,upperfunc*)
Shade((*lowerfunc,upperfunc,resolution*)
Shade((*lowerfunc,upperfunc,resolution,Xleft*)
Shade((*lowerfunc,upperfunc,resolution,Xleft,Xright*)

For example, **Shade(X³–8X,X–2):Shade(X–2,X³–8X,2,-2,5)** displays:

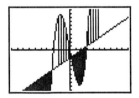

Drawing Circles

While a graph is displayed, **Circle(** lets you define a circle on the graph using the cursor. If a graph is not displayed, the instruction is copied to the Home screen.

Directly on a Graph

1. When a graph is displayed, select **Circle(** from the DRAW DRAW menu (item 9).

2. Position the cursor at the center of the circle you want to draw. Press [ENTER].

3. Move the cursor to a point on the circumference. Press [ENTER]. The circle is drawn on the graph.

To continue to draw circles, repeat steps 2 and 3. To cancel **Circle(** press [CLEAR].

Because this circle is drawn on the display and is independent of the WINDOW values (unlike the **Circle(** instruction, see below), it appears as a circle.

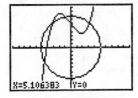

From the Home Screen or a Program

Circle((DRAW DRAW item 9) draws a circle with center (X,Y) and *radius* (these values can be expressions).

Circle(X,Y,*radius***)**

Note: When the **Circle(** instruction is used from a program, the drawn circle may not look like a circle because it is drawn with respect to the current WINDOW values. For example, in the standard viewing WINDOW, **Circle(0,0,7)** displays:

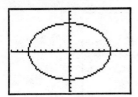

Placing Text on a Graph

While a graph is displayed, **Text(** lets you place text on it. If a graph is not displayed, the instruction **Text(** is copied to the Home screen.

Directly on a Graph

1. When a graph is displayed, select **Text(** from the DRAW DRAW menu.

2. Position the cursor where you want the text to begin.

3. Type the characters. You may enter TI-82 functions and instructions. The font is proportional, so the exact number of characters you can place is variable. As you type, the characters are placed on top of the graph.

To cancel **Text(**, press $\boxed{\text{CLEAR}}$.

From the Home Screen or a Program

Text((DRAW DRAW item 0) places the characters in *text* (which can include TI-82 functions and instructions, except →) on the current graph. The upper left of the first character is at pixel (*row,column*), where *row* is an integer between 0 and 57 (which can be an expression) and *column* is an integer between 0 and 94 (which can be an expression).

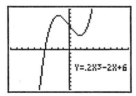

Text(*row,column,value,value* . . .**)**

value may be text enclosed in " marks or an expression, which will be evaluated and the result displayed with up to 10 characters. For example, if **Y1=.2X³−2X+6** is the only selected function, **Text(42,52,"Y=.2X³−2X+6")** displays:

Split Screen

In **Split** screen MODE, the maximum value of *row* is 25.

Using Pen to Draw on a Graph

While a graph is displayed, **Pen** lets you draw directly on the graph with the cursor.

Using Pen

Pen draws directly on a graph. It is not accessible from the Home screen or a program.

1. When a graph is displayed, select **Pen** from the DRAW DRAW menu (item A).

2. Position the cursor where you want to begin drawing. Press [ENTER] to turn the pen on.

3. As you move the cursor, it draws on the graph, turning on each point that the cursor crosses.

4. Press [ENTER] to turn the pen off. Move the cursor to a new position where you want to begin drawing again.

To continue to draw on the graph with the pen, repeat steps 2, 3, and 4. To cancel **Pen**, press [CLEAR].

For example, **Pen** was used to create the arrow pointing to the local minimum of the selected function.

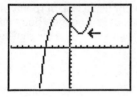

Drawing Points

To display the DRAW POINTS menu, press [2nd] [DRAW] [▶].
What happens when you select an item from this menu is
dependent on whether or not a graph is displayed when
you access the menu, as described under each
operation.

DRAW POINTS Menu

```
DRAW  POINTS  STO
1: Pt-On(           Turn on a point
2: Pt-Off(          Turn off a point
3: Pt-Change(       Toggle a point on or off
4: Pxl-On(          Turn on a pixel
5: Pxl-Off(         Turn off a pixel
6: Pxl-Change(      Toggle a pixel on or off
7: pxl-Test(        Return 1 if pixel is on, 0 if off
```

Directly on a Graph

1. When a graph is displayed, select **Pt-On(** from the
   DRAW POINTS menu.

2. Position the cursor at the location on the display where
   you want to draw the point. Press [ENTER]. The point is
   drawn.

To continue to draw points, repeat step 2. To cancel
Pt-On(, press [CLEAR].

Pt-Off(
Pt-Change(

The procedure for using **Pt-Off(** (point off) to turn off
(erase) a point and **Pt-Change(** (point change) to toggle
(reverse) a point on and off is the same as for **Pt-On.**

Pt-Off(X,Y**)**
Pt-Change(X,Y**)**

From the Home Screen or a Program

Pt-On((point on) turns on the point at (**X**=X,**Y**=Y).

Pt-On(X,Y**)**

Drawing Pixels

The Pxl (pixel) operations let you turn on, turn off, or reverse a pixel (a dot) on the graph using the cursor. The instruction must be entered on the Home screen or in the program editor.

TI-82 Pixels

Turning Pixels On and Off

The pixel instructions are not interactive. **Pxl-On(** (pixel on) (DRAW POINTS item 9) turns on the pixel at (*row,column*), where *row* is an integer between 0 and 62 and *column* is an integer between 0 and 94.

Pxl-On(*row,column***)**
Pxl-Off(*row,column***)**
Pxl-Change(*row,column***)**

pxl-Test(

pxl-Test((pixel test) (DRAW POINTS item 7) returns 1 if a pixel (*row,column*) is On or 0 if it is Off on the current graph. *row* must be an integer between 0 and 62. *column* must be an integer between 0 and 94.

pxl-Test(*row,column***)**

Split Screen

In **Split** screen MODE, the maximum value of *row* is 30 in **Pxl-On(, Pxl-Off(, Pxl-Change(,** and **pxl-Test(.**

Storing and Recalling Graph Pictures

Press [2nd] [DRAW] [◄] to display the DRAW STO menu. You
can store an image of the current display and
superimpose that image onto a displayed graph at a later
time from the Home screen or a program.

**DRAW STO
Menu**

```
DRAW POINTS STO
1:StorePic          Store the current picture
2:RecallPic         Recall a saved picture
3:StoreGDB          Store the current graph database
4:RecallGDB         Recall a saved graph database
```

**Storing a Graph
Picture**

A picture includes drawn elements, plotted functions,
axes, and tick marks. The picture does not include axis
labels, lower and upper bound indicators, prompts, or
cursor coordinates. Any parts of the display "hidden" by
these are stored with the picture.

1. Press [2nd] [DRAW] [◄] (to display the DRAW STO menu)
   1 (to select **StorePic**). **StorePic** is copied to the Home
   screen or program editor.

2. Press [VARS] **4** (to display the VARS PIC menu). Select
   Pic1, **Pic2**, **Pic3**, **Pic4**, **Pic5**, or **Pic6**.

   StorePic Pic$n$

3. Press [ENTER]. The current graph is displayed and the
   picture is stored.

**Recalling a
Graph Picture**

1. Press [2nd] [DRAW] [◄] (to display the DRAW STO menu)
   2 (to select **RecallPic**). **RecallPic** is copied to the Home
   screen or program editor.

2. Press [VARS] **4** (to display the VARS PIC menu). Select
   Pic1, **Pic2**, **Pic3**, **Pic4**, **Pic5**, or **Pic6**.

   RecallPic Pic$n$

3. Press [ENTER]. The current graph is displayed if
   necessary, and the picture is superimposed.

Note: Pictures are drawings. You cannot TRACE any curve
on a picture.

**Deleting a
Graph Picture**

Graph pictures are deleted from memory through the MEM
menu (Chapter 15.)

Storing and Recalling Graph Databases

A graph database is the set of elements that define a particular graph. The graph can be recreated from these elements. You can store up to six graph databases and recall any of them to recreate a graph at a later time.

Graph Databases

The elements of a graph database are:

- Graphing MODE.

- WINDOW variables and WINDOW FORMAT.

- All functions in the Y= list, and whether they are selected.

Graph databases do not include any drawn items or any Stat Plot definitions.

Storing a Graph Database

1. Press [2nd] [DRAW] [◄] (to display the DRAW STO menu) 3 (to select **StoreGDB**). **StoreGDB** is copied to the Home screen or program editor.

2. Press [VARS] 3 (to display the VARS GDB menu). Select **GDB1, GDB2, GDB3, GDB4, GDB5,** or **GDB6.**

3. Press [ENTER]. The current database is stored.

StoreGDB GDBn

Recalling a Graph Database

Caution: When you recall a graph database, all existing Y= functions are replaced. You may want to store the current Y= functions to another database before recalling a stored database.

1. Press [2nd] [DRAW] [◄] (to display the DRAW STO menu) 4 (to select **RecallGDB**). **RecallGDB** is copied to the Home screen or program editor.

2. Press [VARS] 3 (to display the VARS GDB menu). Select **GDB1, GDB2, GDB3, GDB4, GDB5,** or **GDB6.**

RecallGDB GDBn

3. Press [ENTER]. The new graph database replaces the current one. The new graph is not plotted. (The TI-82 changes graphing MODE automatically, if necessary.)

Deleting a Graph Database

Graph databases are deleted from memory through the MEM menu (Chapter 15.)

Clearing a Drawing

All points, lines, and shading drawn on a graph with
DRAW operations are temporary. They remain only until
you execute a ClrDraw (clear drawing) instruction or a
change prompts Smart Graph to replot the graph, at
which time all drawn elements are erased.

**When a Graph
is Displayed**

To clear drawings from the currently displayed graph,
select **ClrDraw** from the DRAW DRAW menu (item 1). The
current graph is plotted and displayed immediately with no
drawn elements.

**From the Home
Screen or a
Program**

Begin on a blank line on the Home screen or in the
program editor. Select **ClrDraw** from the DRAW DRAW
menu (item 1). The instruction is copied to the cursor
location.

When the instruction is executed, it clears all drawings
from the current graph and displays the message Done.
The next time you display the graph, all drawn points,
lines, circles, and shaded areas will be gone.

Note: Before you clear drawings, you can store them with
StorePic (page 8-14).

Chapter 9: Split Screen

On the TI-82, you can simultaneously display a graph (including a stat plot) and an editor such as the Home screen, Y= editor, list editor, or table editor.

Chapter Contents

Getting Started: Polynomial Coefficients

Getting Started is a fast-paced introduction. Read the chapter for details.

Use the split screen capability to explore the behavior of the graph of a polynomial as the coefficients change.

---

1. In **Func** MODE, press [Y=] to display the Y= screen. Press .1 [X,T,θ] [MATH] 3 (to select ^{3}) [−] 2 [X,T,θ] [+] 6 [ENTER] to enter the polynomial **.1X³−2X+6**.

2. Press [MODE] to enter display the MODE screen. Press [▼] [▼] [▼] [▼] [▼] [▼] [▶] [ENTER] to set the screen to **Split**.

3. Press [ZOOM] 6 (to select **ZStandard**). The TI-82 split screen is displayed. The current graph is plotted in the standard viewing WINDOW (just compressed) and displayed on the top half of the display. The bottom half is blank.

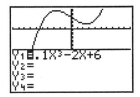

4. Press [▶] to activate the free-moving cursor.

5. Press [Y=]. The Y= editor displays on the bottom half of the display and the cursor moves to the Y= editor.

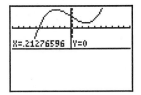

6. Press [▶] to move the cursor over the 1. Press **5**. The graph does not change.

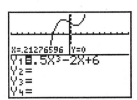

7. Press [GRAPH] to plot the new graph. This also moves the cursor to the upper window. Press [▶] to see the free-moving cursor.

Using Split Screen

Once you have selected split screen, it remains in effect until you change it. A split-screen display may be replaced temporarily by a full-screen display. When you press a key in split-screen MODE, the cursor automatically moves to the correct half of the display for that key.

Setting Screen MODE

To change the screen MODE from **FullScreen** to **Split** or vice versa, you must use the MODE screen.

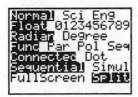

Split Screen: Top

The top half displays the graph screen (any MODE).

The cursor is placed in the upper half of the display by GRAPH, TRACE, a ZOOM operation, or a CALC operation.

Split Screen: Bottom

The bottom half displays an editor.

- Home screen (4 lines)
- Y= editor (4 lines)
- Table (2 rows)
- STAT list editor (2 rows)
- WINDOW (3 settings, can be scrolled)

The cursor is placed in the bottom half of the display whenever a key is pressed that moves to one of these displays.

Exceptions

The split screen will be replaced temporarily by a full-screen display for:

- Full-screen menus
- MODE screen, WINDOW FORMAT screen
- Matrix editor
- TABLE SETUP, SET UP CALCS, STAT PLOTS
- Program editor
- Memory management

Using Split Screen (Continued)

TI-82 Pixels

```
 (0,0)        (0,94)

 (30,0)       (30,94)



```

DRAW Pixels Instructions

The maximum value of *row* is 30 in the **Pxl-On(**, **Pxl-Off(**,and **Pxl-Change(** instructions and the **pxl-Test(** function when MODE is **Split**.

Pxl-On(*row*,*column***)**

DRAW Text Instruction

The maximum value of *row* is 25 in the **Text(** instruction when MODE is **Split**.

Text(*row*,*column*,"*text*"**)**

PRGM Output Instruction

The maximum value of *row* is 4 in the **Output(** instruction when MODE is **Split**.

Output(*row*,*column*,"*text*"**)**

Setting Screen MODE from the Home Screen or a Program

To set screen MODE from a program, press MODE on a blank line in the program editor and select **FullScreen** or **Split**. The instruction is copied to the cursor location. The MODE is set when the instruction is encountered during execution and remains in effect after the program is done

Chapter 10: Matrices

This chapter describes the matrix features of the TI-82. The TI-82 can store up to five matrices. A matrix, depending on available memory, may have up to 99 rows or columns.

Chapter Contents

Getting Started: Systems of Linear Equations

Getting Started is a fast-paced introduction. Read the chapter for details.

Find the solution of x + 2y + 3z = 3 and 2x + 3y + 4z = 3. On the TI-82, you can solve a system of linear equations by entering the coefficients as elements in a matrix and then using the matrix row operations to obtain the reduced row echelon form.

1. Press [MATRX]. Press ▶ ▶ to display the MATRX EDIT menu. Press **1** to select [**A**] to edit matrix [**A**]

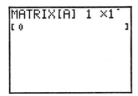

2. Press **2** [ENTER] **4** [ENTER] to define a 2×4 matrix. The rectangular cursor indicates the current element. The ellipses points at the right indicate that one or more additional columns exist.

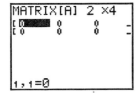

3. Press **1** [ENTER] to enter the first element. The rectangular cursor moves to the second column of the first row.

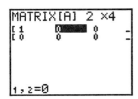

4. Press **2** [ENTER] **3** [ENTER] **3** [ENTER] to complete the top row.

5. Press **2** [ENTER] **3** [ENTER] **4** [ENTER] **3** [ENTER] to enter the bottom row.

6. Press [2nd] [QUIT] to return to the Home screen. Begin on a blank line. Press [MATRX] [▶] to display the MATRX MATH menu. Press [▼] until the bottom items on the menu are shown, then select ***row+(** (item A). ***row+(** is copied to the Home screen.

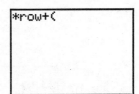

7. Press [(-)] 2 [,]. Press [MATRX] 1 (to select [A] from the MATRX NAMES menu). Press [,] 1 [,] 2 [)] [ENTER]. This multiplies row 1 by -2 and adds it to row 2. The resulting matrix is displayed and stored in **Ans**. The value of [A] is not changed.

```
*row+(-2,[A],1,2
)
     [[1  2  3  3 ]
      [0 -1 -2 -3]]
```

8. Press [MATRX] [▶] to display the MATRX MATH menu. Select ***row(** (item 0) and then press [(-)] 1 [,] [2nd] [Ans] [,] 2 [)] [ENTER]. This multiplies row 2 of the matrix in **Ans** by -1. Again, the resulting matrix is displayed and stored in **Ans**.

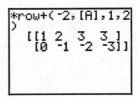

9. Press [MATRX] [▶]. Select ***row+(** (item A). Press [(-)] 2 [,] [2nd] [Ans] [,] 2 [,] 1 [)] [ENTER]. This multiplies row 2 of the matrix in **Ans** by -2 and adds it to row 1. The resulting reduced row-echelon form of the matrix is displayed and stored in **Ans**.

```
*row(-1,Ans,2)
     [[1  2  3  3]
      [0  1  2  3]]
*row+(-2,Ans,2,1
)
     [[1  0 -1 -3]
      [0  1  2  3]]
```

$$1x \quad -1z = {}^-3 \quad \text{so} \quad x = {}^-3 + z$$
$$1y + 2z = 3 \qquad\qquad y = 3 - 2z$$

Defining a Matrix

A matrix is a two-dimensional array. You can display, enter, or edit a matrix in the matrix editor. The TI-82 has five matrix variables: [A], [B], [C], [D], or [E]. You can define a matrix directly in an expression.

Selecting a Matrix

To define or display a matrix in the editor, you first must select the name of the matrix.

1. Press MATRX ▶ ▶ to display the MATRX EDIT menu.

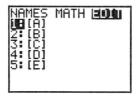

2. Select the matrix you want to define (either [A], [B], [C], [D], or [E]). The MATRX EDIT screen appears.

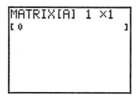

Accepting or Changing Matrix Dimensions

The dimensions of the matrix (row × column) are displayed on the top line. When you select a matrix to define, the cursor is on the row dimension. You must accept or change the dimensions each time you enter or edit a matrix. A "new" matrix has dimension 1×1.

1. Accept or change the number of rows.

   • To accept the number, press ENTER.

   • To change the number, enter the number of rows (up to 99), and then press ENTER.

   The cursor moves to the number of columns.

2. Accept or change the number of columns as above.

   The rectangular cursor moves to the first matrix element.

Viewing Matrix Elements

After the dimensions of the matrix are set, the matrix can be viewed and values can be entered into the matrix elements. In a "new" matrix, all values are zero.

Displaying Matrix Elements

The center portion of the matrix editor displays up to seven rows and three columns of a matrix, showing the values of the elements in abbreviated form if necessary. The full value of the current element (indicated by the rectangular cursor) is shown on the bottom line.

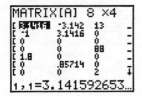

An 8×4 matrix is shown. The ellipses marks and ↓ in the right column indicate additional rows and columns.

Leaving the MATRX Edit Screen

To leave the MATRX edit screen:

- Select another screen by pressing the appropriate key.

- Press [2nd] [QUIT] to return to the Home screen.

Deleting a Matrix

Matrices are deleted from memory through the MEM menu (Chapter 15).

Editing Matrix Elements

The matrix editor has two "contexts," viewing and editing. The current context determines the result of a keypress.

Viewing a Matrix

In viewing context, you can move quickly from one matrix element to the next. The full value of the current element is displayed on the bottom line.

Viewing Context Keys

◄ or ►	Moves the rectangular cursor within the current row.
▼ or ▲	Moves the rectangular cursor within the current column. On the top row, ▲ moves cursor to the column dimension. On the column dimension, moves cursor to the row dimension.
[ENTER]	Switches to editing context; activates the edit cursor on the bottom line.
[CLEAR]	Switches to editing context; clears the value on the bottom line.
Any entry character	Switches to editing context; clears the value on the bottom line; copies the character to the bottom line.
[2nd] [INS]	Nothing.
[DEL]	Nothing.

Editing a Matrix Element

In editing context, an edit cursor is active on the bottom line, and you can change the value of the current matrix element.

1. Use the cursor-movement keys to move the cursor to the matrix element you want to change.

2. Switch to editing context by pressing [ENTER], [CLEAR], or an entry key.

3. Change the value of the matrix element. You may enter an expression (which is evaluated when you leave the editing context) for the value. **Note:** You can press [CLEAR], followed by [ENTER] to restore the value at the rectangular cursor if you make a mistake.

4. Press [ENTER], [▲], or [▼] to move to another element.

Editing Context Keys

[◄] or [►]	Moves the edit cursor within the value.
[▼] or [▲]	Stores the value on the bottom line to the matrix element; switches to viewing context and moves the rectangular cursor within the column.
[ENTER]	Stores the value on the bottom line to the matrix element; switches to viewing context. Rectangular cursor moves to the next element.
[CLEAR]	Clears the value on the bottom line.
Any entry character	Copies the character to the location of the edit cursor on the bottom line.
[2nd] [INS]	Activates insert cursor.
[DEL]	Deletes the character under the edit cursor on the bottom line.

About Matrices

On the Home screen or in a program, you can use, enter, store, and display matrices.

Using a Matrix in an Expression

To use a matrix in an expression, you may:

• Copy the name from the MATRIX NAMES menu.

• Recall the contents of the matrix into the expression with [2nd] [RCL] (Chapter 1).

• Enter the matrix directly (see below).

Entering a Matrix in an Expression

You can enter, edit, and store a matrix in the MATRIX editor. You also can enter a matrix directly in an expression.

1. Press [2nd] [[] to indicate the beginning of the matrix.

2. Press [2nd] [[] to indicate the beginning of a row.

3. Enter a value (which can be an expression) for each element in the row, separated by commas.

4. Press [2nd] []] to indicate the end of a row.

5. Repeat steps 2 through 4 to enter all of the rows.

6. Press [2nd] []] to indicate the end of the matrix.

Note: The closing]] is not necessary at the end of an expression or preceding →.

[[$element_{1,1}$, ... ,$element_{1,n}$] ... [$element_{m,1}$, ... ,$element_{m,n}$]]

The expression is evaluated when the entry is executed. Commas are required on entry to separate elements, but are not displayed on output.

```
2*[[1,2,3][4,5,6
]]
        [[2  4   6 ]
         [8 10 12]]
```

Displaying a Matrix

To display the contents of a matrix on the Home screen, copy the name from the MATRX NAMES menu and press ENTER.

```
[A]
          [[9 8 7]
           [6 5 4]
           [3 2 1]]
```

If all of a matrix answer does not fit in the display, as indicated by ellipsis marks in the left or right column or ↑ or ↓ in the right column, use ▶, ◀, ▼, and ▲ to display the rest of the matrix.

```
...0000 .1429  0↑
...0000 0.0000 0...
...0000 0.0000 0...
...0000 0.0000 0...
...0000 0.0000 0...
...0000 0.0000 0...
...0000 0.0000 0↓
```

Copying One Matrix to Another

To copy a matrix, store it to another matrix. (Access the names on the MATRX NAMES menu.)

```
[A]→[B]
```

Accessing a Matrix Element

You can store a value to (or recall a value from) a specific matrix element on the Home screen or from a program. The element must be within the currently defined matrix dimensions.

matrix(*row,column***)**

```
0→[A](2,3):[A]
          [[9 8 7]
           [6 5 0]
           [3 2 1]]
```

Matrix Math Functions

You can use many of the math functions on the
keyboard, MATH MATH menu, and the MATH NUM menu
with matrices. However, the dimensions must be
appropriate.

+ (Add)
− (Subtract)

To add (+) or subtract (−) matrices, the dimensions must
be the same. The answer is a matrix in which the elements
are the sum or difference of the individual elements.

matrixA+matrixB
matrixA−matrixB

∗ (Multiply)

To multiply (×) two matrices together, the column
dimension of *matrixA* must match the row dimension of
matrixB.

matrixA∗matrixB

Multiplying a *matrix* by a *value* or a *value* by a *matrix*
returns a matrix in which each element of *matrix* is
multiplied by *value*.

matrix∗value
value∗matrix

- (Negate)

Negating a matrix ((-)) returns a matrix in which the sign
of every element is changed (reversed).

−matrix

abs

abs (absolute value, 2nd [ABS]) returns a matrix containing
the absolute value of each element of *matrix*.

abs *matrix*

round(	**round(** (MATH NUM menu) returns a matrix. It rounds every element in *matrix* to *#decimals*. If *#decimals* is omitted, the elements are rounded to 10 digits.
	round(*matrix*,*#decimals*) **round(***matrix*)
⁻¹ (Inverse)	Use the **⁻¹** function ($\boxed{x^{-1}}$) to invert a matrix (**^-1** is not valid). *matrix* must be square. The determinant cannot equal zero.
	matrix⁻¹
Powers	To raise a matrix to a power, *matrix* must be square. You may use **²**, **³**, or **^***n* (*n* between **0** and **255**).
	*matrix*² *matrix*³ *matrix*^*power*
Relational Operations	To compare two matrices using the relational operations = and ≠, they must have the same dimensions. = and ≠ compare *matrixA* and *matrixB* on an element-by-element basis. The other relational operations are not valid with matrices.
	matrixA=*matrixB* returns **1** if every comparison is true; it returns **0** if any comparison is false.
	matrixA≠*matrixB* returns **1** if at least one comparison is false.
iPart fPart int	**iPart**, **fPart**, and **int** (MATH NUM menu) return a matrix containing the integer part, fractional part, or greatest integer of each element of *matrix*.
	iPart *matrix* **fPart** *matrix* **int** *matrix*

MATRX MATH Operations

Pressing [MATRX] [▶] accesses the matrix math operations on the MATRX MATH menu.

MATRX MATH Menu

NAMES **MATH** EDIT

1: det		Calculates the determinant
2:ᵀ		Transposes the matrix
3:dim		Returns the matrix dimension
4:Fill(		Fills all elements with a constant
5:identity		Returns the identity matrix
6:randM(		Returns a random matrix
7:augment(		Augments two matrices
8:rowSwap(		Swaps two rows of a matrix
9:row+(		Adds two rows, stores in second row
0:*row(		Multiplies row by a number
A:*row+(		Multiplies row, adds to second row

det

det (determinant) returns the determinant (a real number) of a square *matrix*.

det *matrix*

ᵀ (Transpose)

ᵀ (transpose) returns a matrix in which each element(row,column) is swapped with the corresponding element(column,row) of *matrix*.

*matrix*ᵀ

Accessing Matrix Dimensions with dim

dim (dimension) returns a list containing the dimensions ({*rows columns*}) of *matrix*.

dim *matrix*

Note: **dim** *matrix*→L*n*:L*n*(1) returns the number of rows. **dim** *matrix*→L*n*:L*n*(2) returns the number of columns.

```
dim [[2,7,1][-8,
3,1]]
             {2 3}
dim [[2,7,1][-8,
3,1]]→L₁:L₁(1)
                 2
```

Creating a Matrix with dim

dim (MATRIX MATH item 3) is used with $\boxed{\text{STO►}}$ to create new *matrixname* of dimensions *rows* × *columns* with all elements equal to zero.

{*rows*,*columns*}→**dim** *matrixname*

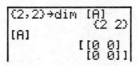

Redimensioning a Matrix with dim

dim is used with $\boxed{\text{STO►}}$ to redimension existing *matrixname* to dimensions *rows* × *columns*. The elements in the old *matrixname* that are within the new dimensions are not changed. Any additional elements that are created are zeros.

{*rows*,*columns*}→**dim** *matrixname*

Fill(

Fill((MATRIX MATH item 4) stores *value* to every element in *matrixname*.

Fill(*value*,*matrixname***)**

identity

identity (MATRIX MATH item 5) returns the identity matrix of *dimension* rows × *dimension* columns.

identity *dimension*

randM(

randM((create random matrix, MATRIX MATH item 6) returns a *rows* × *columns* matrix of random one-digit integers (-9 to 9). The values are controlled by the **rand** function.

randM(*rows*,*columns***)**

```
0→rand:randM(2,2
)-1►Frac
     [[1/7   1/8]
      [-1/7  0  ]]
```

augment(

augment((MATRIX MATH item 7) concatenates *matrixA* and *matrixB*. The number of rows in *matrixA* must equal the number of rows in *matrixB*.

augment(*matrixA,matrixB***)**

```
[[1,2][3,4]]→[A]
:[[5,6][7,8]]→[B
]:augment([A],[B
])
     [[1 2 5 6]
      [3 4 7 8]]
```

Row Operations

The row operations, which can be used in an expression, do not change *matrix* in memory. All row numbers and values can be entered as expressions.

rowSwap(

rowSwap((MATRIX MATH item 8) returns a matrix. It swaps *rowA* and *rowB* of *matrix*.

rowSwap(*matrix,rowA,rowB***)**

row+(

row+((row addition, MATRIX MATH item 9) returns a matrix. It adds *rowA* and *rowB* of *matrix* and stores the answer in *rowB*.

row+(*matrix,rowA,rowB***)**

*row(

*row((row multiplication, MATRIX MATH item 0) returns a matrix. It multiplies *row* of *matrix* by *value* and stores the answer in *row*.

*row(*value,matrix,row***)**

*row+(

*row+((multiply and add row, MATRIX MATH item A) returns a matrix. It multiplies *rowA* of *matrix* by *value*, adds it to *rowB*, and stores the answer in *rowB*.

*row+(*value,matrix,rowA,rowB***)**

```
[[1,2][3,4]→[B]
          [[1 2]
           [3 4]]
*row+(3,[B],1,2)
          [[1 2 ]
           [6 10]]
```

Chapter 11: Lists

This chapter describes the list features of the TI-82.
The TI-82 can store up to six lists. A list, depending on
available memory, may have up to 99 elements.

Chapter Contents

Getting Started: Generating a Sequence

Getting Started is a fast-paced introduction. Read the chapter for details.

Calculate the first eight terms of the sequence $1/N^2$ and display in fractional form.

1. Begin on a blank line on the Home screen. Press [2nd] [LIST] to display the LIST OPS menu.

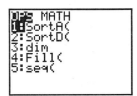

2. Press **5** to select **seq(**. The function name is copied to the cursor location on the Home screen.

3. Press **1** [÷] [ALPHA] **A** [x^2] [,] [ALPHA] **A** [,] **1** [,] **8** [,] **1** [)] [STO►] [2nd] [L1]. Press [ENTER] to generate the list and store it in **L1**. The list is displayed on the Home screen.

```
seq(1/A²,A,1,8,1
)→L1
{1 .25 .1111111…
```

4. Use [►] to scroll the list to see all of the elements.

5. Press [MATH] **1** (to select **►Frac**). On the Home screen, **Ans** is typed automatically, followed by **►Frac**.

```
seq(1/A²,A,1,8,1
)→L1
…7778 .02040816…
Ans►Frac
```

6. Press [ENTER] to show the sequence in fractional form. Use [►] to scroll the list to see all of the elements.

```
seq(1/A²,A,1,8,1
)→L1
…7778 .02040816…
Ans►Frac
…1/36 1/49 1/64}
```

About Lists

The TI-82 has six list variables in memory: L1, L2, L3, L4, L5, and L6. On the Home screen or in a program, you can use, enter, store, and display lists. The list names are on the keyboard.

Using a List in an Expression

To use a list in an expression, you may:

- Use the name of the list (**L1**, **L2**, **L3**, **L4**, **L5**, or **L6**).

```
5+L1█
```

- Enter the list directly (see below).

```
5+L1+{1,2,3}█
```

- Press [2nd] [RCL], enter the name of the list, and then press [ENTER] to recall the contents of the list into the expression at the cursor location.

```
5+L1+{1,2,3}+{2,
10,32}█
```

Entering a List in an Expression

1. Press [2nd] [{] to indicate the beginning of the list.

2. Enter a value (which can be an expression) for each element in the list, separated by commas.

3. Press [2nd] [}] to indicate the end of the list.

```
2*{1,2+3,4²}
        {2 10 32}
```

The expression is evaluated when the entry is executed. Commas are required on entry to separate elements, but are not displayed on output. The closing **}** is not necessary at the end of an expression or preceding →.

Saving a List in Memory

You can save a list in memory in two ways:

- Enter the list in the STAT list editor (Chapter 12).

- Enter the list on a blank line on the Home screen or in a program (see above), press [STO▶], and then enter the name of the list (**L1**, **L2**, **L3**, **L4**, **L5**, or **L6**).

```
2*{1,2+3,4²}→L6
        {2 10 32}
```

About Lists (Continued)

Displaying a List

To display the contents of a list on the Home screen, enter the name of the list and press ENTER.

If all of a list answer does not fit in the display on the Home screen, as indicated by ellipsis marks in the left or right column, use ▶ and ◀ to display the rest of the list.

```
L₆
{2 10 -1.088042...
```

Copying One List to Another

To copy a list, store it to another list.

```
L₆→L₅
{2 10 -1.088042...
```

Accessing a List Element

You can store a value to (or recall a value from) a specific list element. Enter the name of the list, followed by the number of the element in parentheses. You can store to any element within the currently defined list dimensions or one beyond.

listname(*element*)

```
{1,2,3}→L₃
              {1 2 3}
4→L₃(4)
                    4
L₃
          {1 2 3 4}
```

Lists in Graphing

In graphing, lists are used to graph a family of curves (Chapter 3).

Notes about Using Math Functions with Lists

A list can be used to input several values for certain functions. (Other chapters and Appendix A state if a list is valid.) The function is evaluated for each element in the list, and a list is returned.

- If a list is used with a function, the function must be valid for every element in the list, except in graphing. (In graphing, an invalid element in a list, such as -1 in √{1,0,-1}, is simply ignored.)

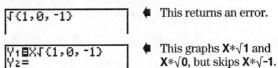

> √{1,0,-1}   ◀ This returns an error.

> Y₁⊟X√{1,0,-1}   ◀ This graphs X∗√1 and
> Y₂=   X∗√0, but skips X∗√-1.

- If two lists are used with a two-argument function, the length of the lists must be the same. The answer is a list in which each element is calculated by evaluating the function using the corresponding elements in the lists.

> {1,2,3}+{4,5,6}
>   {5 7 9}

- If a list and a value are used with a two-argument function, the value is used with each element in the list.

> {1,2,3}+4
>   {5 6 7}

LIST OPS Operations

Pressing [2nd] [LIST] accesses the list operations on the
LIST OPS menu.

**LIST OPS
Menu**

```
OPS MATH
1: SortA(          Sorts lists in ascending order
2: SortD(          Sorts lists in descending order
3: dim             Accesses the list dimension
4: Fill(           Fills all elements with a constant
5: seq(            Creates a sequence
```

Note: **dim** and **Fill(** are the same as **dim** and **Fill(** on the
MATRX MATH menu. **SortA(** and **SortD(** are the same as
SortA(and **SortD(** on the STAT EDIT menu.

**SortA(
SortD(**

SortA((sort ascending) and **SortD(** (sort descending) have
two uses.

• With one *listname*, they sort the elements of an
  existing list and update the list in memory.

• With two to six *listnames*, they sort the first list and
  then sort the remaining lists as dependent lists,
  element-by-element, and update the lists in memory.
  All lists must be the same length.

SortA(*listname*)
SortA(*listnameI,listnameD,listnameD,...*)

```
{5,4,3}→L₃:{1,2,
3}→L₄:SortA(L₃,L
₄):L₃
            {3 4 5}
L₄
            {3 2 1}
```

Accessing List Dimensions with dim	**dim** (dimension) returns the length (number of elements) of *list*.

dim *list*

```
dim {1,3,5,7}
              4
```

Creating a List with dim	**dim** is used with [STO▸] to create new *listname* with dimension *length*. The elements are zeros.

length→**dim** *listname*

```
3→dim L₂
              3
L₂
        {0 0 0}
```

Redimensioning a List with dim	**dim** is used with [STO▸] to redimension existing *listname* to dimension *length*.

- The elements in the old *listname* that are within the new dimension are not changed.

- Any additional elements that are created are zeros.

length→**dim** *listname*

```
{1,3,5,7}→L₄:5→d
im L₄:L₄
       {1 3 5 7 0}
3→dim L₄:L₄
          {1 3 5}
```

Fill(

Fill((LIST OPS item 4) stores *value* to each element in *listname*.

Fill(*value,listname***)**

```
L3
            {3 4 5}
Fill(8,L3)
              Done
L3
          {8 8 8}
```

seq(

seq((sequence, LIST OPS item 5) returns a list in which each element is the value of *expression*, evaluated at *increment*s for *variable* from *begin* to *end*.

seq(*expression,variable,begin,end,increment***)**

```
seq(A²,A,1,11,3)
   {1 16 49 100}
```

variable need not be defined in memory. *increment* can be negative. **seq(** is not valid in the *expression*.

U*n* or **V***n* is not valid in *expression*. To generate a sequence from **U***n* or **V***n*, use **U***n*(*nstart,nstop,nstep*).

LIST MATH Operations

Pressing [2nd] [LIST] [▶] accesses the list math operations on the LIST MATH menu.

LIST MATH Menu

```
OPS MATH
1:min(          Returns minimum element of a list
2:max(          Returns maximum element of a list
3:mean(         Returns mean of a list
4:median(       Returns median of a list
5:sum           Returns sum of all elements in list
6:prod          Returns product of all elements in list
```

Note: **min(** and **max(** are the same as **min(** and **max(** on the MATH NUM menu.

min(
max(

min((minimum) and **max(** (maximum) return the smallest or largest element of *list*. If two lists are compared, it returns a list of the larger of each pair of elements in *listA* and *listB*.

min(list) or **max(**list)
min(listA,listB) or **max(**listA,listB)

```
min({1,2,3},{3,2
,1})
            {1 2 1}
max({1,2,3},{3,2
,1})
            {3 2 3}
```

mean(
median(

mean(returns the mean value of *list*. **median(** returns the median value of *list*.

mean(list) or **median(**list)

If a second list is given, it is interpreted as the *frequency* of the elements in *list*.

mean(list,frequency) or **median(**list,frequency)

```
mean({1,2,3},{3,
2,1})
        1.666666667
median({1,2,3},{
3,2,1})
                1.5
```

LIST MATH Operations (Continued)

---

sum

sum (summation, LIST MATH item 5) returns the sum of the elements in *list*.

sum *list*

```
sum {5,2,3}
            10
```

prod

prod (LIST MATH item 6) turns product of the elements of *list*.

prod *list*

```
prod {5,2,3}
            30
```

Sums and Products of Numeric Sequences

You can combine **sum** or **prod** with **seq(** to obtain:

$$\sum_{x=lower}^{upper} expression(x) \qquad \prod_{x=lower}^{upper} expression(x)$$

To evaluate $\Sigma\, 2^{(N-1)}$ from N=1 to 4:

```
sum seq(2^(N-1),
N,1,4,1)
            15
```

Chapter 12: Statistics

This chapter describes the tools for analyzing statistical data on the TI-82. These include entering lists of data, calculating statistical results, fitting data to a model, and plotting data.

Getting Started: Building Height and City Size

Getting Started is a fast-paced introduction. Read the chapter for details.

Determine a linear equation to fit the data below. Enter and plot the data and determine the best line, then predict how many buildings of more than 12 stories you would expect to find in a city of 300,000 people. Begin by entering the data in the STAT list editor and sorting it.

Population	Buildings>12 stories
150,000	4
500,000	31
800,000	42
250,000	9
500,000	20
750,000	55
950,000	73

1. To clear any existing lists, press [STAT] 4 (to copy **ClrList** to the Home screen) and then press [2nd] [L1] [,] [2nd] [L2] [,] [2nd] [L3] [,] [2nd] [L4] [,] [2nd] [L5] [,] [2nd] [L6] [ENTER].

2. Press [STAT] to display the STAT EDIT menu.

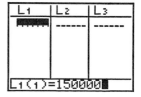

3. Press **1** (to select **Edit...**). The STAT list editor is displayed.

   Press **150000**. As you type, the value is displayed on the bottom line.

4. Press [ENTER]. The value is shown in the first element of **L1** and the cursor moves to the second element in the same list.

   Press **500000** [ENTER] **800000** [ENTER] **250000** [ENTER] **500000** [ENTER] **750000** [ENTER] **950000** [ENTER] to enter the remaining elements of **L1**.

5. Press ▶ to move to the first element of list **L₂**.

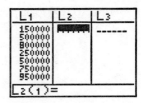

6. Press **4** ENTER **31** ENTER **42** ENTER **9** ENTER **20** ENTER **55** ENTER **73** ENTER to enter the elements of **L₂**.

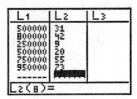

7. You can sort the data by size of city. Press STAT **2** (to select **SortA(**, which is copied to the Home screen) 2nd [L₁] (to select the independent list) , 2nd [L₂] (to select the dependent list)) ENTER.

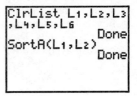

8. The lists have been updated in memory. Press STAT **1** to use the STAT list editor to display the lists.

Getting Started: Building Height and City Size (Cont.)

After entering and sorting the data, set up the statistical calculations, then perform the calculations, storing the equations in the Y= list.

9. Press STAT ▶ to display the STAT CALC menu.

```
EDIT CALC
1█1-Var Stats
2:2-Var Stats
3:SetUp…
4:Med-Med
5:LinReg(ax+b)
6:QuadReg
7↓CubicReg
```

10. Press **3** (to select **SetUp...**).

    The SET UP CALCS screen appears. Xlist for 2-Var should be **L1**; Ylist should be **L2**; and Freq should be **1**.

```
SET UP CALCS
1-Var Stats
Xlist:█L1█L2 L3 L4 L5 L6
Freq:█L1 L2 L3 L4 L5 L6
2-Var Stats
Xlist:█L1█L2 L3 L4 L5 L6
Ylist:L1 █L2█L3 L4 L5 L6
Freq:█L1 L2 L3 L4 L5 L6
```

11. Press STAT ▶ **4** (to select **Med-Med**). The instruction is copied to the Home screen. Press ENTER to calculate a line fitting the data using the SET UP CALCS settings. The model coefficients are displayed on the Home screen.

```
Med-Med
y=ax+b
a=7.5555556ᴇ-5
b=-8
```

12. In **Func** MODE, press Y= to display the Y= editor. Clear **Y1** and **Y2** if necessary.

    Press VARS to display the VARS screen.

```
VARS
1█Window…
2:Zoom…
3:GDB…
4:Picture…
5:Statistics…
6:Table…
```

13. Press **5** (to select **Statistics...**) and ▶ ▶ to display the VARS EQ menu.

```
X/Y Σ EQ BOX PTS
1:a
2:b
3:c
4:d
5:e
6:r
7:RegEQ
```

14. Press **7** (to select **RegEQ**). The regression equation for the current model equation (which was calculated using **Med-Med**) is copied to **Y1**.

```
Y1◻7.55555555555
56E-5X+-8
Y2=
Y3=
Y4=
Y5=
Y6=
Y7=
```

15. Press STAT ▶ **5** (to select **LinReg(ax+b)**). The instruction is copied to the Home screen. Press ENTER to calculate the least-squares linear regression.

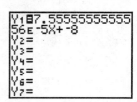

```
LinReg
  y=ax+b
  a=8.1560773E-5
  b=-12.01243094
  r=.9573174921
```

16. Press Y= (to display the Y= editor) ENTER (to move to **Y2**) VARS (to display the VARS menu) **5** (to select **Statistics...**) ▶ ▶ (to display the VARS EQ menu) **7** (to select **RegEQ**). The current model equation (calculated using **LinReg(ax+b)**) is copied to **Y2**.

```
Y1◻7.55555555555
56E-5X+-8
Y2◻8.15607734806
63E-5X+-12.01243
0939227◼
Y3=
Y4=
Y5=
```

To plot statistical data, you must enter the data in lists and then define the plot. If you have done calculations to fit the data to one or more models and stored the resulting equations in the Y= list, the data and the equations can be shown and traced simultaneously.

17. Press [2nd] [STAT PLOT] to display the STAT PLOTS screen.

18. Press **1** (to display the Plot1 screen). Press [ENTER] to turn Plot1 **On**. Leave Type as a scatter plot, Xlist as **L1**, and Ylist as **L2** and Mark as a □.

19. Press [ZOOM] **9** (to select **ZoomStat**). **ZoomStat** examines the data for all currently selected Stat Plots and adjusts the viewing WINDOW to include all points, which are shown on the current graph. (This also plots the regression equations in **Y1** and **Y2**.)

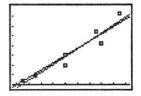

20. Press [TRACE]. Press ▶ to trace the points in Plot1, as indicated by **P1** in the upper right corner of the display.

Press ▼ to move to **Y1**. Press ▼ again to move to **Y2**.

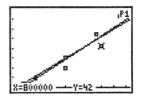

You can enter expressions to define lists in the STAT list editor. For
example, you can define predicted values and residuals.

21. To tell which line better fits the data,
    look at the residuals for both models.
    Press [STAT] 1 to display the STAT list
    editor. Press [▶] [▶] [▲] to move the cursor
    onto the name **L3**.

    Press [2nd] [Y-VARS] **1** (to select
    Function...) **1** (to select **Y1**) [(] [2nd] [L1]
    [)]. This defines **L3** as the values
    predicted by the **Med-Med** line.

L1	L2	L3
150000	4	------
250000	9	
500000	20	
500000	31	
750000	55	
800000	42	
950000	73	

L3=Y1(L1)

22. Press [ENTER] to store the values in **L3**.

L1	L2	L3
150000	4	3.3333
250000	9	10.889
500000	20	29.778
500000	31	29.778
750000	55	48.667
800000	42	52.444
950000	73	63.778

L3(1)=3.3333333...

23. To store the residuals for **Med-Med** in
    L4, press [▶] [▲] (to move the cursor onto
    the name **L4**) [2nd] [L2] (the observed) [−]
    [2nd] [L3] (the predicted) [ENTER].

L2	L3	L4
4	3.3333	.66667
9	10.889	-1.889
20	29.778	-9.778
31	29.778	1.2222
55	48.667	6.3333
42	52.444	-10.44
73	63.778	9.2222

L4(1)=.66666666...

24. Press [▶] [▲] to move onto **L5**. Press
    [2nd] [Y-VARS] **1** (to select **Function...**)
    2 (to select **Y2**) [(] [2nd] [L1] [)] [ENTER].
    This defines **L5** as the values predicted
    by the **LinReg(ax+b)** line.

25. Press [▶] [▲] (to move the cursor onto
    the name **L6**) [2nd] [L2] (the observed) [−]
    [2nd] [L5] (the predicted) [ENTER] to
    evaluate and store the residuals for
    LinReg(ax+b) in **L6**.

L4	L5	L6
.66667	.22169	3.7783
-1.889	8.3778	.62224
-9.778	28.768	-8.768
1.2222	28.768	2.232
6.3333	49.158	5.8419
-10.44	53.236	-11.24
9.2222	65.47	7.5297

L6(1)=3.7783149...

Getting Started: Building Height and City Size (Cont.)

You can use the TI-82 to compare different models on the same data set.

26. Press [2nd] [STAT PLOT]. Press **1** to select Plot1. Press [▶] [ENTER] to turn the plot off.

    Press [2nd] [STAT PLOT]. Press **2** to select Plot2. Press [ENTER] to turn the plot on. Press [▼] [▼] [ENTER] to define Xlist as **L1**. Press [▼] [▶] [▶] [▶] [ENTER] to define Ylist as **L4**. Leave Mark as a □.

27. Press [2nd] [STAT PLOT]. Press **3** to select Plot3. Press [ENTER] to turn the plot on. Press [▼] [▼] [ENTER] to define Xlist as **L1**. Press [▼] [▶] [▶] [▶] [▶] [▶] [ENTER] to define Ylist as **L6**. Press [▼] [▶] [ENTER] to define Mark as **+**.

    Press [2nd] [STAT PLOT] to view the settings.

28. Press [Y=] [◀] [ENTER] [▼] [ENTER] to turn off **Y1** and **Y2**.

    Press [ZOOM] **9** to plot the residuals. □ marks the residuals from **Med-Med** and **+** marks the residuals from **LinReg**.

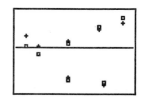

29. Press [2nd] [QUIT] to return to the Home screen. Press [MATH] [▶] **1** (to select round() [2nd] [Y-VARS] **1** (to select Function...) **1** (to select **Y1**) [(] **300000** [)] [,] **0** [)] [ENTER]. The value of **Y1** (**Med-Med** model) for **X**=300,000, rounded to 0 decimal places (whole buildings), is shown.

    Press [2nd] [ENTRY] [▲] [▶] [2nd] [Y-VARS] **1** **2** [ENTER]. The value of **Y2** (**LinReg(ax+b)** model) for **X**=300,000 is shown.

Setting Up a Statistical Analysis

The data for statistical analyses is stored in lists. The TI-82 has six list variables in memory that you can use in stat calculations. Several types of statistical analyses are available.

Steps

1. Enter the stat data in list(s) (pages 12-9 through 12-12).

2. Set up statistical calculations (page 12-13).

3. Calculate the statistical variables or fit the data to a model (page 12-14 through 12-17).

4. Plot the data (page 12-18 through 12-21).

Displaying the STAT List Editor

To display the STAT list editor, press [STAT] and then press **1** or [ENTER] to select **Edit...** from the STAT EDIT menu.

The top line displays the names of the lists (even if the list is empty). The center portion of the STAT list editor displays up to seven elements of three lists, showing the values of the elements in abbreviated form if necessary. The full value of the current element (indicated by the rectangular cursor) is shown on the bottom line.

Leaving the STAT List Editor

To leave the STAT list editor:

• Select another screen by pressing the appropriate key.

• Press [2nd] [QUIT] to return to the Home screen.

Deleting a List

You can delete the contents of a list in several ways:

• Use the **ClrList** instruction (page 12-12).

• Through the MEM menu (Chapter 16).

• In the STAT editor, press [▲] to move onto the list name, and press [CLEAR] [ENTER].

• In the STAT editor, delete each element.

• On a command line, enter **0→dim** *listname*.

Viewing List Elements

The STAT list editor has two "contexts," viewing and editing. The current context determines the result of a keypress.

Viewing Context Keys

In viewing context, you can move quickly from one list element to the next. The full value of the current element is displayed on the bottom line.

◄ or ►	Moves the rectangular cursor within the current row.
▼ or ▲	Moves the rectangular cursor within the current column. On row 1, ▲ moves the cursor to the list name and shows the entire list in display input format, but the list cannot be scrolled).
ENTER	Switches to editing context; activates the edit cursor on the bottom line.
CLEAR	Switches to editing context; clears the value on the bottom line.
Any entry character	Switches to editing context; clears the value on the bottom line; copies the character to the bottom line.
2nd [INS]	Inserts a list element (value is zero).
DEL	Deletes the current list element (closes up list).

Editing List Elements

In the editing context, an edit cursor is active on the bottom line, and you can change the value of the current list element. You can also move onto the list name and edit the entire list at once.

Editing Context Keys

◄ or ►	Moves the edit cursor within the value.
[CLEAR]	Clears the value on the bottom line.
Any entry character	Copies the character to the location of the edit cursor on the bottom line. If it is the first character typed, the value on the bottom line is cleared.
[2nd] [INS]	Activates insert cursor.
[DEL]	Deletes character.
[ENTER]	Stores the value on the bottom line to the list element; switches to viewing context. Rectangular cursor moves to the next element.
▼ or ▲	Stores the value on the bottom line to the list element; switches to viewing context and moves the rectangular cursor within the column.

Editing a List Element

1. Move the rectangular cursor to the element you want to change.

2. Switch to editing context.

   • Press [ENTER] to change the value by inserting, deleting, or typing over digits.

   • Press [CLEAR] to clear the entire value so you can enter a new value. **Note:** You can press [CLEAR], followed by [ENTER] to restore the value at the rectangular cursor if you make a mistake.

   • Press an entry key, such as a number or letter, to begin an entry. This automatically clears the value.

3. Enter the value. You may enter an expression (which is evaluated when you leave editing context).

4. Press [ENTER], ▲, or ▼ to move to another element.

STAT EDIT Menu

Pressing [STAT] accesses the STAT list editor and several instructions for use with lists.

STAT EDIT Menu

EDIT CALC	
1:Edit...	Displays list editor (page 12-9).
2:SortA(	Sorts list in descending order
3:SortD(	Sorts list in ascending order
4:ClrList	Deletes all elements of list

Note: SortA(and **SortD(** are the same as **SortA(** and **SortD(** on the LIST OPS menu.

SortA(
SortD(

SortA((sort ascending) and **SortD(** (sort descending) have two uses.

• With one *listname*, they sort the elements of an existing list and update the list in memory.

• With two to six *listnames*, they sort the first list and then sort the remaining lists as dependent lists, element by element, and update the lists in memory. All lists must be the same length.

SortA(*listname*)
SortA(*listnameI,listnameD,listnameD, . . .*)

```
{5,4,3}→L₃:{1,2,
3}→L₄:SortA(L₃,L
₄):L₃
              {3 4 5}
L₄
              {3 2 1}
```

ClrList

ClrList clears (deletes) the elements of one or more *listnames*.

ClrList *listnameA,listnameB,* . . .

Statistical Analysis

Pressing [STAT] [▶] accesses the STAT CALC menu, where you set up and perform statistical calculations. The TI-82 can analyze one-variable or two-variable statistics. Both can have associated frequencies.

STAT CALC Menu

```
EDIT CALC
1:1-Var Stats        Calculates 1-variable statistics
2:2-Var Stats        Calculates 2-variable statistics
3:SetUp...           Defines lists to use in calculations
4:Med-Med            Calculates median-median line
5:LinReg(ax+b)       Fits data to linear model
6:QuadReg            Fits data to quadratic model
7:CubicReg           Fits data to cubic model
8:QuartReg           Fits data to quartic model
9:LinReg(a+bx)       Fits data to linear model
0:LnReg              Fits data to logarithmic model
A:ExpReg             Fits data to exponential model
B:PwrReg             Fits data to power model
```

SET UP CALCS Screen

When you select **SetUp...**, the SET UP CALCS screen appears, where you can define a statistical analysis.

```
SET UP CALCS
1-Var Stats
Xlist:L1 L2 L3 L4 L5 L6
Freq:1 L1 L2 L3 L4 L5 L6
2-Var Stats
Xlist:L1 L2 L3 L4 L5 L6
Ylist:L1 L2 L3 L4 L5 L6
Freq:1 L1 L2 L3 L4 L5 L6
```

- **1-Var Stats** (one-variable statistics) analyzes data with one measured variable.

- **2-Var Stats** (two-variable statistics) analyzes paired data between which there is a relationship. **Xlist** is the independent variable. **Ylist** is the dependent variable.

- **Freq** (frequency of occurrence) is a list of integers between 0 and 99 (inclusive). **Freq** is optional; the default is **1**. It is valid for one-variable or two-variable statistics.

Note: You can override SET UP CALCS settings by specifying the name(s) of the list(s) after the statistical calculation instruction (Appendix A).

Changing Settings

To change a setting on the SET UP CALCS screen, use [▼], [▲], [▶], and [◀] to position the cursor and then press [ENTER].

Statistical Variables

The statistical variables are calculated as indicated below. Some are displayed when 1-Var Stats or 2-Var Stats are calculated. You can access these variables for use in expressions through the $\boxed{\text{VARS}}$ Statistics... menus. If a list is edited or the type of analysis is changed, all statistical variables are cleared.

Variables	1-Var Stats	2-Var Stats	Other	VARS Menu
mean of **x** values	$\bar{x}$	$\bar{x}$		X/Y
sum of **x** values	Σ**x**	Σ**x**		Σ
sum of **x²** values	Σ**x²**	Σ**x²**		Σ
sample standard deviation of **x**	**Sx**	**Sx**		X/Y
population standard deviation of **x**	σ**x**	σ**x**		X/Y
number of data points	**n**	**n**		X/Y
mean of **y** values		$\bar{y}$		X/Y
sum of **y** values		Σ**y**		Σ
sum of **y²** values		Σ**y²**		Σ
sample standard deviation of **y**		**Sy**		X/Y
population standard deviation of **y**		σ**y**		X/Y
sum of **x** * **y**		Σ**xy**		Σ
minimum of **x** values	**minX**	**minX**		X/Y
maximum of **x** values	**maxX**	**maxX**		X/Y
minimum of **y** values		**minY**		X/Y
maximum of **y** values		**maxY**		X/Y
1st quartile	**Q₁**			BOX
median	**Med**			BOX
3rd quartile	**Q₃**			BOX
regression/fit coefficients			**a, b**	EQ
polynomial coefficients			**a, b, c, d, e**	EQ
correlation coefficient			**r**	EQ
regression equation			**RegEQ**	EQ
summary points (**Med-Med** only)			**x₁, y₁, x₂, y₂, x₃, y₃**	PTS

Q₁ and Q₃   The quartile **Q₁** is the median of the ordinals to the left of **Med**. The quartile **Q₃** is the median of the ordinals to the right of **Med**.

Types of Statistical Analysis

The SET UP CALCS settings are used for statistical analyses. You can override SET UP CALCS settings by specifying the name(s) of the list(s) and frequency after the statistical calculation instruction (Appendix A).

1-Var Stats   **1-Var Stats** (one-variable statistics, STAT CALC item 1) calculates statistical variables as indicated on the previous page.

2-Var Stats   **2-Var Stats** (two-variable statistics, STAT CALC item 2) calculates statistical variables as indicated on the previous page.

Med-Med   **Med-Med** (median-median, STAT CALC item 4) fits the data to the model **y=ax+b** using the median-median line (resistant line) technique, calculating the summary points x_1, y_1, x_2, y_2, x_3, and y_3. It displays **a** (slope) and **b** (y-intercept).

LinReg (ax+b)   **LinReg (ax+b)** (linear regression, STAT CALC item 5) fits the data to the model **y=ax+b** using a least-squares fit and **x** and **y**. It displays **a** (slope), **b** (y-intercept), and **r** (correlation coefficient).

QuadReg   **QuadReg** (quadratic regression, STAT CALC item 6) fits the data to the second-order polynomial $y=ax^2+bx+c$. It displays **a**, **b**, and **c**. For three points the equation is a polynomial fit; for four or more, it is a polynomial regression. At least three points are required.

CubicReg   **CubicReg** (cubic regression, STAT CALC item 7) fits the data to the third-order polynomial $y=ax^3+bx^2+cx+d$. It displays **a**, **b**, **c**, and **d**. For four points the equation is a polynomial fit; for five or more, it is a polynomial regression. At least four points are required.

QuartReg   **QuartReg** (quartic regression, STAT CALC item 8) fits the data to the fourth-order polynomial $y=ax^4+bx^3+cx^2+dx+e$. It displays **a**, **b**, **c**, **d**, and **e**. For five points the equation is a polynomial fit; for six or more, it is a polynomial regression. At least five points are required.

Types of Statistical Analysis (Continued)

LinReg **(a+bx)**	**LinReg (a+bx)** (linear regression, STAT CALC item 9) fits the data to the model equation **y=a+bx** using a least-squares fit and **x** and **y**. It displays **a** (**y**-intercept), **b** (slope), and **r** (correlation coefficient).
LnReg	**LnReg** (logarithmic regression, STAT CALC item 0) fits the data to the model equation **y=a+b ln(x)** using a least-squares fit and transformed values **ln(x)** and **y**. It displays **a**, **b**, and **r** (correlation coefficient).
ExpReg	**ExpReg** (exponential regression, STAT CALC item A) fits the data to the model equation $\mathbf{y=ab^x}$ using a least-squares fit and transformed values **x** and **ln(y)**. It displays **a** (y-intercept), **b**, and **r** (correlation coefficient).
PwrReg	**PwrReg** (power regression, STAT CALC item B) fits the data to the model equation $\mathbf{y=ax^b}$ using a least-squares fit and transformed values **ln(x)** and **ln(y)**. It displays **a**, **b**, and **r** (correlation coefficient).

Statistical Analysis in a Program

You can enter statistical data, calculate statistical results, and fit data to models from a program.

Entering Stat Data

Enter statistical data into lists directly (Chapter 11).

Statistical Calculations

1. On a blank line in the program editor, select the type of calculation from the STAT CALC menu.

2. You can enter the names of the lists to use in the calculation or use the lists defined in SET UP CALCS. **Note:** You cannot access SET UP CALCS from the program editor.

```
PROGRAM:STATS
:LinReg(ax+b) L₁
,L₂
```

Statistical Plotting

You can plot statistical data that you have entered in lists. The types of plots available include scatter plots, x-y lines, box and whisker plots, and histograms. You can define up to three plots at a time.

Steps

1. Enter the stat data in list(s) (page 12-9 through 12-12 and Chapter 11).

2. Set up statistical calculations (page 12-13) and calculate the statistical variables or fit the data to a model (page 12-14 through 12-17), if desired.

3. Select or deselect Y= equations as appropriate (Chapter 3).

4. Define the stat plot (page 12-21).

5. Turn plot(s) on, if necessary (page 12-21).

6. Define the viewing WINDOW (page 12-21 and Chapter 3).

7. Display and explore the graph (Chapter 3).

Scatter Plot

Scatter plots the data points from Xlist and Ylist as coordinate pairs, showing each point as a box (□), cross (+), or dot (•). Xlist and Ylist must be the same length. They can be the same list. Freq does not apply.

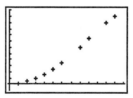

xyLine

xyLine is a **Scatter** plot in which the data points are plotted and connected in the order in which they appear in Xlist and Ylist. You may want to sort the lists with **SortA(** or **Sort(D** before plotting.

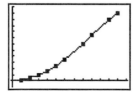

Boxplot

Boxplot plots one-variable data. The whiskers on the plot extend from the minimum data point in the set (**minX**) to the first quartile (**Q₁**) and from the third quartile (**Q₃**) to the maximum point (**maxX**). The box is defined by **Q₁**, the median (**Med**), and **Q₃**. (page 12-14)

Box plots ignore **Ymin** and **Ymax**, but are plotted with respect to **Xmin** and **Xmax**. When two box plots are plotted, the first plots in the middle and the second plots in the bottom. When three box plots are plotted, the first plots on the top and the third plots on the bottom.

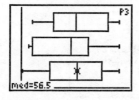

Histogram

Histogram plots one-variable data. **Xscl** determines the width of each bar, beginning at **Xmin**. **ZoomStat** adjusts **Xmin** and **Xmax** to include all values, but does not change **Xscl**. (**Xmax–Xmin**)/**Xscl** must be ≤ 47. A value occurring on the edge of a bar is counted in the bar to the right.

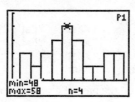

Statistical Plotting (Continued)

Defining the Plots

1. Press [2nd] [STAT PLOT]. The STAT PLOTS screen shows the current plot definitions.

2. Select the plot to define (Plot1, Plot2, or Plot3).

3. If you wish to plot the statistical data immediately, select **On**. You can define a plot at any time and leave it **Off**. The definition will be available in the future.

4. Select the type of plot. The options change appropriately:

	Xlist	Ylist		Mark
• **Scatter:**	Xlist	Ylist		Mark
• **xyLine:**	Xlist	Ylist		Mark
• **Boxplot:**	Xlist		Freq	
• **Histogram:**	Xlist		Freq	

5. Depending on the type of plot, select the options:

   - **Xlist** (independent data)
   - **Ylist** (dependent data)
   - **Freq** (frequency, **1** is used if not specified)
   - **Mark** (□, +, or •)

Turning Plots Off or On	**PlotsOff** and **PlotsOn** allow you to turn stat plots on or off from the Home screen or a program. Used without *plot#*, they turn all plots on or all plots off. Used with *plot#*, they turn specific plots on or off.

PlotsOff or **PlotsOn**
PlotsOff *plot#*,*plot#*, . . .
PlotsOn *plot#*

For example, **PlotsOff:PlotsOn 3** turns all plots off and then turns Plot3 on.

Defining the Viewing WINDOW	Stat plots are displayed on the current graph. You may define the viewing WINDOW by pressing WINDOW and then entering values for the WINDOW variables.

ZoomStat redefines the viewing WINDOW so that all statistical data points are displayed. For one-variable plots (**Histogram** and **Box plot**), only **Xmin** and **Xmax** are adjusted. If the top of the histogram is not shown, use TRACE to determine the value for **Ymax**.

Tracing a Stat Plot	When you TRACE a **Scatter** plot or **xyLIne**, tracing begins at the first element in the lists.

When you TRACE a **Box** plot, tracing begins at **Med** (the median). Press ◁ to trace to **Q1** and **minX**. Press ▷ to trace to **Q3** and **maxX**.

When you TRACE a **Histogram,** the cursor moves from the top center of each column.

When you press ▲ or ▼ to move to another plot or Y= function, tracing moves to the current or beginning point on that plot (not the nearest pixel).

Statistical Plotting in a Program

You may define a plot, select or deselect a plot, and display a plot from a program

Stat Plots

To display a stat plot, you may define the plot(s), then turn on the plot(s), and then display the graph. (If you do not define the plot, the current definitions are used).

For example:

```
PROGRAM:STAT
:{55,62,88,43,94
,61}→L₁
:Plot1(Boxplot,L
1)
:FnOff
:PlotsOn 1
:ZoomStat
```

Defining a Stat Plot

1. Begin on a blank line in the program editor. Press [2nd] [STAT PLOT] to display the STAT PLOTS menu.

2. Select the plot to define. **Plot1**, **Plot2**, or **Plot3** is copied to the cursor location.

3. Press [2nd] [STAT PLOT] [▶] to display the STAT TYPES menu. Select the type of plot. **Scatter**, **xyLIne**, **Boxplot**, or **Histogram** is copied to the cursor location.

4. Press [,] then enter list names. See Appendix A for the appropriate options.

5. Select the type of mark (for **Scatter** or **xyLine**).

Displaying a Stat Plot

To display a plot, use the **DispGraph** instruction or any of the ZOOM instructions.

Chapter 13: Programming

This chapter describes specific programming instructions and how to enter and execute programs on the TI-82.

Chapter Contents

Getting Started: Family of Curves

Getting Started is a fast-paced introduction. Read the chapter for details.

A program is a set of commands that can be executed sequentially, as if they had been entered from the keyboard. Write a simple program to graph the family of curves 2 sin X, 4 sin X, and 6 sin X.

1. Press PRGM ▷ ▷ to display the PRGM NEW menu.

   ```
   EXEC EDIT NEW
   1∎Create New
   ```

2. Press ENTER (to select **Create New...**). Type **S I N E S** as the name of the program (the keyboard is in ALPHA-LOCK), and press ENTER.

   You are now in the program editor. Note the : (colon) in the first column of the second line to indicate that this is the beginning of a command line.

   ```
   PROGRAM:SINES
   :∎
   ```

3. Press ALPHA ["] (above +) 2nd [{] 2 ,
   4 , 6 2nd [}] SIN X,T,Θ ALPHA ["] STO►
   2nd [Y-VARS]. Press ENTER (to select **Function...**). Press ENTER (to select **Y1**).

   This instruction stores the function **{2,4,6}sin X** to **Y1**.

   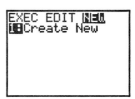

4. Press ENTER to complete the instruction and move to the next line. The : (colon) indicates the beginning of the second command line.

5. Press ZOOM. The ZOOM menu appears, just as it does elsewhere. Press **6** (to select **ZStandard**). The instruction **ZStandard** is copied to the cursor location. Press ENTER to complete the instruction.

   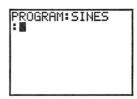

6. Press TRACE. The instruction **Trace** is copied to the cursor location. Press ENTER to complete the instruction.

7. Press 2nd [QUIT] to return to the Home screen.

8. Press PRGM to display the PRGM menu.

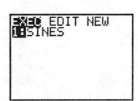

9. Select **SINES**. The instruction **prgmSINES** is copied to the Home screen.

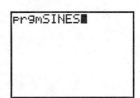

10. Press ENTER to execute the instruction. The three curves are graphed immediately, then the dotted "pause" indicator appears in the upper right of the display to indicate that the program will not resume execution until you press ENTER.

11. Use ◄, ▲, ►, and ▼ to trace the curves.

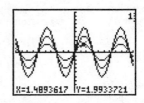

12. When you are done tracing, press ENTER. The program continues. (In this case it ends.) The graph remains on the screen for you to examine.

13. Press Y= to display the Y= editor. Notice that **Y1** now contains the function you stored to it in the program.

About TI-82 Programs

Most features of the TI-82 are accessible from programs.
Programs can access all variables and named items. The
number of programs that the TI-82 can store is limited
only by available memory.

Notes about Programs

On the TI-82, programs are identified by names, up to eight
characters, beginning with a letter.

A program consists of a series of program commands,
which begin with a : (colon). A program command can be
an expression or an instruction.

The TI-82 checks for errors when the program is executed,
not as you enter or edit the program.

Variables, lists, and matrices saved in memory are global.
They can be accessed from all programs. Storing a new
value to a variable, list, or matrix in a program changes the
value in memory during program execution.

As calculations are made in programs, **Ans** is updated, just
as it would be if the calculations were done on the Home
screen. Programs do not update Last Entry as each
command is executed.

"Breaking" a Program

[ON] stops program execution. When you press [ON] to stop
program execution, the ERR: BREAK screen is displayed.

• To go to where the interrupt occurred, select **Goto**.

• To return to the Home screen, select **Quit**.

Memory Management and Erasing Programs

The size of programs you can store is limited only by
available memory. To access the memory management
menu, press [2nd] [MEM] from the Home screen. Memory
status is displayed on the Check RAM... screen. To increase
available memory, delete items, including other programs,
from the MEM DELETE FROM... screen (Chapter 15).

Creating and Executing Programs

The program editor is accessed by pressing [PRGM] and then choosing to create a new program or edit an existing program.

Creating a New Program

1. Press [PRGM] [▶] [▶] to display the PRGM NEW menu. Select **Create New**.

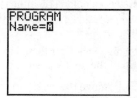

```
PROGRAM
Name=▯
```

2. Enter the name you want for the program (the keyboard is in ALPHA-LOCK), followed by [ENTER]. The name may have one to eight characters (A-Z, 0-9, θ) and must begin with a letter.

3. Enter the program instructions (page 13-6).

Editing a Program

1. Press [PRGM] [▶] to display the PRGM EDIT menu.

2. Select the name of an existing program. The instructions in that program are displayed.

3. Edit the program instructions (page 13-6).

Leaving the Program Editor

When you finish entering or editing a program, press [2nd] [QUIT] to return to the Home screen. You must be on the Home screen to execute a program.

Executing a Program

1. From a blank line on the Home screen, press [PRGM] to display the PRGM EXEC menu.

2. Select the name of an existing program. **prgm** and the name of the program are copied to the Home screen; for example, **prgmSINES**.

3. Press [ENTER] to begin execution of the program.

While the program is executing, the busy indicator is displayed.

Editing Programs

In general, anything that can be executed from the Home screen can be included in a program, and vice versa. A program command always begins with a colon.

Entering Program Commands	A colon indicates the beginning of each program command. To enter more than one instruction on a line, separate them with a colon (Chapter 1), just as on the Home screen. Press [ENTER] to indicate the end of a command line.
	An instruction may be longer than one line on the screen; if so, it will wrap to the next screen line.
	[2nd] [◄] and [2nd] [►] move the cursor to the beginning and end of a command line.
	In the program editor, if you press a key that accesses a menu, the menu screen temporarily replaces the program edit screen. When you make a selection or press [CLEAR], you are returned to the program editor.
Changing	Move the cursor to the command.
	• Position the cursor and then make the changes.
	• Press [CLEAR] to clear (blank) all program commands on the command line (the leading colon is not deleted), and then enter a new program command.
Inserting	To insert a new command line, position the cursor where you want the new line, press [2nd] [INS] to put the TI-82 in insert mode, and press [ENTER].
Deleting	To delete a command line, press [CLEAR] to clear the line and then press [DEL] to delete the colon.
Copying a Program	RCL (Chapter 1) copies (inserts) all of the commands of one program into another, which you then can edit.
	• You can create templates for frequently used groups of instructions, such as setting WINDOW variables.
	• You can make copies of programs.
	To recall a program, press [2nd] [RCL] [PRGM] [◄] to display the PRGM EXEC menu, then select the name of the program and press [ENTER].

PRGM CTL (Control) Instructions

The PRGM CTL (program control) instructions can be accessed only from within the program editor (press PRGM). They direct the flow within an executing program. They make it easy to repeat or skip a group of commands during program execution. When you select an item from the menu, the name is copied to the cursor location.

PRGM CTL Menu

```
CTL I/O EXEC
1:If              Create conditional test
2:Then            Used with If
3:Else            Used with If-Then
4:For(            Create incrementing loop
5:While           Create conditional loop
6:Repeat          Create conditional loop
7:End             Signifies end of loop, If-Then, or Else
8:Pause           Pause program execution
9:Lbl             Define a label
0:Goto            Go to a label
A:IS>(            Increment and skip if greater than
B:DS<(            Decrement and skip if less than
C:Menu(           Define menu items and branches
D:prgm            Execute a program as a subroutine
E:Return          Return from a subroutine
F:Stop            Stops execution
```

Controlling Program Flow

Program control instructions tell the TI-82 which command to execute next in a program. **If, While**, and **Repeat** check a *condition* that you define to determine what command to execute next. *condition* frequently uses relational or Boolean tests (Chapter 2) such as **If A<7:A+1→A** or **If N=1 and M=1:Goto Z**.

If

If is used for testing and branching. If *condition* is false (zero), then the command immediately following it is skipped. If *condition* is true (nonzero), that command is executed. **If** instructions can be nested.

:If *condition*
:*command if true*
:*command*

If-Then   **Then** following an **If** executes a group of commands if *condition* is true (nonzero). **End** identifies the end of the group. (PRGM CTL item 2)

                                     :**If** *condition*
                                     :**Then**
                                     :*command if true*
  :*command if true*
  :**End**
  :*command*

If-Then-Else   **Else** following **If-Then** executes a group of commands if *condition* is false (zero). **End** identifies the end of the group. (PRGM CTL item 3)

  :**If** *condition*
  :**Then**
  :*command if true*
  :*command if true*
  :**Else**
  :*command if false*
  :*command if false*
  :**End**
  :*command*

For(**For(** is used for looping and incrementing. It increments *variable* from *begin* to *end*, by *increment*. *increment* is optional (if not specified, 1 is used) and can be negative (*end*<*begin*). *end* is a maximum or minimum value not to be exceeded. **End** identifies the end of the loop. **For(** loops can be nested. (PRGM CTL item 4)

  :**For(***variable,begin,end,increment***)**
  :*command while end not exceeded*
  :*command while end not exceeded*
  :**End**
  :*command*

For example, **For(A,0,10,2):Disp A^2:End**, displays **0**, **4**, **16**, **36**, **64**, and **100**.

While

While performs a group of commands while *condition* is true. *condition* is frequently a relational test (Chapter 2). *condition* is tested when **While** is encountered. If *condition* is true (nonzero), the program executes a group of commands. **End** signifies the end of the group. If *condition* is false (zero), the program executes the commands following **End**. **While** instructions can be nested. (PRGM CTL item 5)

:**While** *condition*
:*command while condition is true*
:*command while condition is true*
:**End**
:*command*

Repeat

Repeat repeats a group of commands until *condition* is true (nonzero). It is similar to **While**, but *condition* is tested when **End** is encountered; thus the group of commands will always be executed at least once. **Repeat** instructions can be nested. (PRGM CTL item 6)

:**Repeat** *condition*
:*command until condition is true*
:*command until condition is true*
:**End**
:*command*

End

End identifies the end of a group of commands. Each **For**, **While**, **Repeat**, or **Else** loop must have an **End** at the "bottom," as must a **Then** loop without an associated **Else**. (PRGM CTL item 7)

PRGM CTL (Control) Instructions (Cont.)

Pause

Pause suspends execution of the program so you can see answers or graphs. During the pause, the dotted pause indicator displays. Press ENTER to resume execution. (PRGM CTL item 8)

• **Pause** with no *value* temporarily pauses the program. If the instruction **DispGraph** or **Disp** has been executed, then the appropriate screen is displayed.

• **Pause** *value* displays *value*, which can be scrolled, on the current Home screen.

Lbl
Goto

Lbl (label) and **Goto** (go to) are used together for branching.

Lbl specifies the *label* of a command. *label* is one character (A-Z, 0-9, or θ). (PRGM CTL item 9)

Lbl *label*

Goto causes the program to branch to *label* when the **Goto** is encountered. (PRGM CTL item 0)

Goto *label*

IS>(

IS>((increment-and-skip) adds 1 to *variable*; if the answer is greater than *value* (which can be an expression), the next command is skipped. *variable* cannot be a system variable. (PRGM CTL item A)

:**IS>(***variable,value*)
:*command if variable ≤ value*
:*command if variable > value*

DS<(

DS<((decrement-and-skip) subtracts 1 from *variable*; if the answer is less than *value* (which can be an expression), the next command is skipped. *variable* cannot be a system variable. (PRGM CTL item B)

:**DS<(***variable,value*)
:*command if variable ≥ value*
:*command if variable < value*

Menu(

Menu(sets up branching within a program. If **Menu(** is encountered during execution, the menu screen is displayed with the specified menu items, the dotted-bar pause indicator displays, and execution pauses until a menu selection is made. (PRGM CTL item C)

The menu *title* is enclosed in ", followed by up to seven pairs of menu items (*text* enclosed between " marks to display as the menu selection and the *label* to which to branch if that selection is made).

Menu("*title*","*text1*",*label1*,"*text2*",*label2*, . . .**)**

For example, during execution the instruction **Menu("TOSS DICE","FAIR DICE",A,"WEIGHTED DICE",B)** displays:

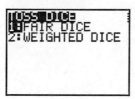

The program pauses until you select **1** or **2**. If you select **2**, for example, the menu disappears and the program continues execution at **Lbl B**.

prgm

prgm is used to enter instructions to execute other programs as subroutines (page 13-18). When you select **prgm**, it is copied to the cursor location. You may then type the letters of a program *name*. It is equivalent to selecting existing programs from the PRGM EXEC menu, but allows you to enter the name of a program that you have not yet created. (PRGM CTL item D)

prgm*name*

Note: You cannot use this command with RCL (page 13-6).

The PRGM CTL (Control) Instructions (Cont.)

Return   **Return** quits the subroutine and returns to the calling program (page 13-18), even if encountered within nested loops. (Any loops are ended.) There is an implied **Return** at the end of any program called as a subroutine. Within the main program, it stops execution and returns to the Home screen. (PRGM CTL item E)

Stop   **Stop** stops execution of a program and returns you to the Home screen. (PRGM CTL item F)

PRGM I/O (Input/Output) Instructions

The PRGM I/O (program input/output) instructions can be accessed only from within the program editor (press PRGM ▶). They control input to and output from a program during execution. They allow you to enter values and display answers during program execution.

PRGM I/O Menu

CTL **I/O** EXEC

1: Input	Enter value or use free-moving cursor
2: Prompt	Prompt for entry of variable values
3: Disp	Display text, value, or Home screen
4: DispGraph	Display the current graph
5: DispTable	Display table
6: Output(	Display text at a specified position
7: getKey	Check the keyboard for a keystroke
8: ClrHome	Clear the display
9: ClrTable	Clear the current table
0: PrintScreen	Print the current screen
A: Get(	Gets variable from another device
B: Send(	Sends variable to another device

Input

- **Input** without *variable* is used to display a graph on which you can use the free-moving cursor.

- **Input** with *variable* or "*string*" and *variable* is used to store a value to a variable.

Displaying a Graph with Input

Input without *variable* displays the current graph. You can move the free-moving cursor, which updates **X** and **Y** (and **R** and θ in PolarGC FORMAT). The dotted-bar pause indicator is displayed. Press ENTER to resume execution.

Storing a Variable Value with Input

Input with *variable* prompts **?** during execution. *variable* may be a real number, list, matrix or Y= function. Enter a value (which can be an expression) and press ENTER. The value is evaluated and stored to *variable*, and the program resumes execution. If *variable* is Y*n* or other Y= functions, enter " and then the expression, which will be stored to the Y= function as entered.

Input *variable*

You can display a *string* of up to 16 characters as a prompt. Enter a value and press ENTER. The value is stored to *variable*, and the program resumes execution.

Input "*string*",*variable*

Disp

- **Disp** (display) with no *value* displays the Home screen.

- **Disp** with one or more *values* displays text and values.

Displaying the Home Screen

Disp with no *value* displays the Home screen.

Disp

Displaying Values and Messages

Disp with one or more *values* displays the value of each.

Disp *value,value,value...*

- If *value* is an expression, it is evaluated and then displayed on the right of the following line according to the current MODE settings.

- If *value* is text (up to 16 characters) within " marks, it displays on the left of the following line. Text cannot include ➔.

For example, **Disp "THE ANSWER IS",π/2** displays:

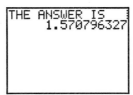

If **Pause** is encountered after **Disp**, the program halts temporarily so you can examine the screen. Press ENTER to resume execution.

Note: If a matrix or list is too large to display in its entirety, ... is displayed in the rightmost column, but the matrix or list cannot be scrolled. (To scroll, use the **Pause** instruction instead.)

Prompt

During execution **Prompt** displays each *variable*, one at a time, followed by **=?**. Enter a value and then press $\boxed{\text{ENTER}}$ for each *variable*. The values are stored, and the program resumes execution. (PRGM I/O item 2)

Prompt *variableA,variableB,* . . .

For example, **Prompt Xmin, Xmax, Ymin, Ymax** allows the user to enter values for the viewing WINDOW.

If an expression is entered in response to **Prompt**, the expression is evaluated and then stored. **Y***n* and other Y= functions are not valid with **Prompt**.

DispGraph

DispGraph (display graph) displays the current graph. If **Pause** is encountered after **DispGraph**, the program halts temporarily so you can examine the screen. Press $\boxed{\text{ENTER}}$ to resume execution. (PRGM I/O item 4)

DispTable

DispTable (display table) displays the current table. The program halts temporarily so you can examine the screen. Press $\boxed{\text{ENTER}}$ to resume execution. (PRGM I/O item 5)

Output(

Output(displays *text* or a *value* on the current Home screen beginning at *line* (1 through 8) and *column* (1 through 16), typing over any existing characters. You may wish to precede **Output(** with **ClrHome** (page 13-17). Expressions are evaluated and values are displayed according to the current MODE settings. Matrices are displayed in entry format and wrap to the next line. *text* cannot include →. (PRGM I/O item 6)

Output(*line,column,***"***text***")**
Output(*line,column,value***)**

In **Split** screen MODE, the maximum value of *row* is 4 for **Output(**.

getKey

getKey returns a number corresponding to the last key pressed, according to the diagram below. If no key has been pressed, it returns 0. **getKey** can be used inside loops to transfer control; for example, to create video games. (PRGM I/O item 7)

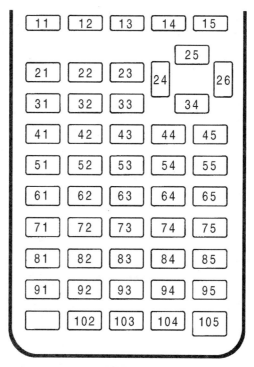

Note: You can press ON at any time to act as a break during execution (page 13-4).

ClrHome

ClrHome (clear Home screen) clears the Home screen during execution and places the cursor in the upper left corner, but program execution does not pause unless **Pause** is encountered. (PRGM I/O item 8)

ClrTable

ClrTable (clear table) clears the table in the table editor during execution and places the cursor in the upper left corner, but program execution does not pause unless **Pause** is encountered. (PRGM I/O item 9)

PrintScreen

PrintScreen (print screen) prints the current screen on a printer attached to an IBM®-compatible computer or a Macintosh® if you are using TI-GRAPH LINK™ software (Chapter 16). The dotted-bar pause indicator displays. Press ENTER to resume execution. **PrintScreen** acts like **Pause** if you are not using TI-GRAPH LINK. (PRGM I/O item 0)

Get(

Get(gets the contents of *variable* on another TI-82 and stores it to *variable* on the receiving TI-82. *variable* may be a number, list, list element, matrix, matrix element, Y= variable, graph database or picture. **Get(** also can be used to get data from an external compatible device. (PRGM I/O item A)

Get(*variable***)**

Send(

Send(sends the contents of *variable* to an external compatible device. It cannot be used to send to another TI-82. (PRGM I/O item B)

Send(*variable***)**

Calling Other Programs

On the TI-82, any program can be called from another program as a subroutine. Enter the name of the program to use as a subroutine on a line by itself.

Calling a Program from Another Program

To call one program from another, begin on a blank line in the program editor and do one of the following:

- Press [PRGM] ◄ to display the PRGM EXEC menu and select the name of the program. **prgm** and the name are copied to the current cursor location.

- Select **prgm** from the PRGM CTL menu and then type the letters of the program *name* (page 13-11).

prgm*name*

When this instruction is encountered during execution, the next command that the program executes is the first command in the second program. It returns to the subsequent command in the first program when it encounters either a **Return** instruction or the implied **Return** at the end.

```
PROGRAM:VOLCYL      ⇒  PROGRAM:AREACIRC
:Prompt D          ⇑  :D/2→R
:Prompt H          ⇑  :π*R²→A
:prgmAREACIRC ⇒    ⇑  :Return ⇒ ⇒ ⇒
⇒ :A*H→V                              ⇓
⇑ :Disp V                             ⇓
⇐ ⇐ ⇐ ⇐ ⇐ ⇐ ⇐ ⇐ ⇐ ⇐ ⇐ ⇐ ⇐ ⇐
```

Notes about Calling Programs

Variables are global.

label used with **Goto** and **Lbl** is local to the program in which it is located. *label* in one program is not "known" by another program. You cannot use **Goto** to branch to a *label* in another program.

Return exits a subroutine and returns to the calling program, even if encountered within nested loops.

Chapter 14: Applications

This chapter contains application examples that incorporate features described in the preceding chapters. Several of the examples use programs.

Left-Brain, Right-Brain Test Results

An experiment found a significant difference between the ability of boys and girls to identify objects held in their left hands (which are controlled by the right side of the brain) versus their right hands (which are controlled by the left side of the brain). The TI Graphics team decided to conduct a similar test for adult men and women.

Problem

30 small objects were chosen. Coworkers held half of the objects (which they were not allowed to see) in their left hands and half in their right hands and tried to identify them. Use box plots to compare visually the results from the table below.

Correct Responses

Women Left	Women Right	Men Left	Men Right
8	4	7	12
9	3	8	6
12	7	7	12
11	12	5	12
10	11	7	7
8	11	8	11
12	13	11	12
7	12	4	8
9	11	10	12
11	12	14	11
		13	9
		5	9

Procedure

1. Press [STAT] **1** (to select **Edit...**). If there are values in any of the lists, follow the procedure to clear lists described in Chapter 12. Enter the values for the number of correct guesses each woman made with her left hand in **L1**.

2. Press [▶] to move to **L2** and enter the scores that each woman made with her right hand.

3. Enter the men's scores in **L3** and **L4**.

4. Press [2nd] [STAT PLOT] **1** (to select **Plot1**). Turn on Plot1 and define it as a box plot, using **L1**. Press [2nd] [STAT PLOT] **2** (to select **Plot2**). Turn on Plot2 and define it as a box plot, using **L2**.

5. Press [Y=] and turn off any selected functions. Press [WINDOW]. Set **Xscl=1, Ymin=0, Yscl=0**. (Ignore the other WINDOW settings, which will be set by **ZoomStat**.)

Procedure (Continued)

6. Press $\boxed{\text{ZOOM}}$ **9** (to select **ZoomStat**). This adjusts the viewing WINDOW and displays the box plots for the women's results (left on top).

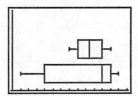

7. Press $\boxed{\text{TRACE}}$ and examine **minX, Q1, Med, Q3,** and **maxX** for each plot. What is the median for the left hand? For the right hand? Does it appear that the women guessed correctly more often with the left or right hand?

8. Examine the men's results. Press $\boxed{\text{2nd}}$ [STAT PLOT] and redefine Plot1 to use **L3** and Plot2 to use **L4**. Press $\boxed{\text{TRACE}}$. What difference do you see between the plots?

9. Compare the left-hand results. Press $\boxed{\text{2nd}}$ [STAT PLOT] and redefine Plot1 to use **L1** and Plot2 to use **L3**. Press $\boxed{\text{TRACE}}$. Were women or men better at guessing with their left hands?

10. Compare the right-hand results. Press $\boxed{\text{2nd}}$ [STAT PLOT] and redefine Plot1 to use **L2** and Plot2 to use **L4**. Press $\boxed{\text{TRACE}}$. Were women or men better at guessing with their right hands?

The original experiment found that boys did not guess as well with their right hands, while girls guessed equally well with either hand. That is not what these box plots showed for adults. Do you think that this is because adults have learned to adapt or because our sample was not large enough?

Speeding Tickets

The fine for speeding in your area is $50 plus $5 per mile per hour over the limit for the first 10 miles, plus $10 per mile per hour for the next 10 miles, plus $20 per mile thereafter. Graph the piecewise function that describes the cost of the ticket in a 45-mile-per-hour zone.

Problem

The fine (**Y**) as a function of miles per hour (**X**) is:

$$Y = 0 \qquad\qquad\qquad\qquad\qquad\qquad 0 < X \le 45$$
$$Y = 50 + 5\,(X - 45) \qquad\qquad\qquad 45 < X \le 55$$
$$Y = 50 + 5 * 10 + 10\,(X - 55) \qquad 55 < X \le 65$$
$$Y = 50 + 5 * 10 + 10 * 10 + 20\,(X - 65) \qquad 65 < X$$

Procedure

1. Press [MODE]. Select **Func**, **Dot**, and the defaults. Press [2nd] [STAT PLOT] and turn off all stat plots.

2. Press [Y=]. Turn off any selected functions. The TEST operations are used to define piecewise functions. Enter the Y= function to describe the fine.

   Y₁=(50+5(X−45))(45<X)(X≤55)
   +(100+10(X−55))(55<X)(X≤65)
   +(200+20(X−65))(65<X)

3. Press [WINDOW] and set **Xmin = -2**, **Xscl = 10**, **Ymin = -5**, and **Yscl = 10**. Ignore **Xmax** and **Ymax**. (They are set by ΔX and ΔY in step 4.)

4. Press [2nd] [QUIT] to return to the Home screen and store **1** to ΔX and **5** to ΔY. (ΔX and ΔY, the distance between the centers of adjacent pixels, are on the VARS Window... menu.) Defining ΔX and ΔY as integers produces nice values for TRACE.

5. Press [TRACE] to plot the functions. At what speed does the ticket exceed $250?

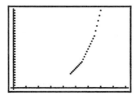

Buying a Car, Now or Later?

You have identified the car you would like to buy, which costs $8,000. You can afford payments of $250 per month. You can either borrow the money at 10% annual interest (compounded monthly) and buy the car now, or invest the payments at 6% and pay cash for the car later. How long will it take to pay for the car each way?

Procedure

1. Press [MODE]. Select the default MODE settings. Press [2nd] [STAT PLOT] and turn off all stat plots.

2. On the Home screen, store the values of the periodic interest rates.

   .06 / 12 → I   .10 / 12 → J

3. Press [Y=]. Turn off all functions and enter the formula to describe investing the money.

   Y₂=250((1+I)^X−1)/I

4. Enter the formula to describe making car payments.

   Y₃=8000−250(1−(1+J)^-X)/J

5. To determine how many months will be required to pay cash, press [2nd] [QUIT] to return to the Home screen. Solve the equation (the amount saved less $8000) for **X**, using 36 months as the guess. (**solve(** is on the MATH MATH menu.)

   solve(Y₂−8000,X,36)

6. To determine how long it will take to pay off the loan, enter:

   solve(Y₃,X,36)

7. To calculate how much you would pay in total if you got a loan, press [×] **250**, which multiplies the months to pay off the loan (in **Ans**) by the payment amount.

8. Press [2nd] [TABLE] to examine the amount saved versus the amount still owed for each time period.

9. Press [WINDOW]. Set the viewing WINDOW.

   Xmin = 0   Ymin = 0
   Xmax = 47   Ymax = 8000
   Xscl = 12   Yscl = 1000

10. Press [TRACE] to examine the amounts graphically.

Graphing Inequalities

Examine the inequality $.4X^3-3X+5<.2X+4$ graphically. Use the TEST functions to explore the values of X where the inequality is true and where it is false.

Procedure

1. Press MODE. Select **Dot, Simul**, and the default MODE settings. Press 2nd [STAT PLOT] and turn off all stat plots.

2. Press Y=. Turn off all functions. Enter the left side of the inequality as **Y4** and the right side as **Y5**.

   $Y4=.4X^3-3X+5$
   $Y5=.2X+4$

3. Enter the statement of the inequality as **Y6**. This function evaluates to 1 if true and 0 if false.

   $Y6=Y4<Y5$

4. Press ZOOM **6** to graph the inequality in the standard WINDOW.

5. Press TRACE ▼ ▼ to move to **Y6** and trace the inequality, observing the value of **Y**.

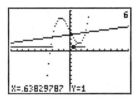

6. Press Y=. Turn off **Y4**, **Y5**, and **Y6**. Enter equations to graph only the inequality.

   $Y7=Y6Y4$
   $Y8=Y6Y5$

7. Press TRACE. Notice that the values of **Y7** and **Y8** are zero where the inequality is false.

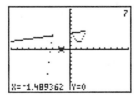

Solving a System of Nonlinear Equations

Solve the equation $X^3-2X=2\cos X$ graphically. Stated another way, solve the system of two equations and two unknowns: $Y=X^3-2X$ and $Y=2\cos X$. Use the ZOOM factors to control the decimal places displayed on the graph.

Procedure

1. Press [MODE]. Select the default MODE settings. Press [2nd] [STAT PLOT] and turn off all stat plots. Press [Y=]. Turn off all functions and enter the functions $Y_7=X^3-2X$ and $Y_8=2\cos X$.

2. Press [ZOOM] and select **ZDecimal**. The display shows that there are two areas that might contain solutions (points where the two functions appear to intersect).

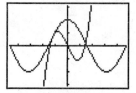

3. Press [ZOOM] [▶] and select **SetFactors...** from the ZOOM MEMORY menu. Set **XFact=10** and **YFact=10**.

4. Press [ZOOM] **2** (to select **Zoom In**). Use [▶], [◀], [▲], and [▼] to position the free-moving cursor on the apparent intersection of the functions on the right side of the display. As you move the cursor, note that the **X** and **Y** coordinates have one decimal place.

5. Press [ENTER] to zoom in. Move the cursor over the intersection. As you move the cursor, note that now the **X** and **Y** coordinates have two decimal places.

6. Press [ENTER] to zoom in again. Move the free-moving cursor to a point exactly on the intersection. Note the number of decimal places.

7. Press [2nd] [CALC] and select **intersect**. Press [ENTER] to select the First curve and [ENTER] to select the Second curve. Now trace to a Guess near the intersection and press [ENTER]. What are the coordinates of the intersection?

8. Press [ZOOM] and select **ZDecimal** to redisplay the original graph.

9. Press [ZOOM]. Select **Zoom In** and explore as above the other apparent intersection.

Program: Sierpinski Triangle

This program creates a drawing of a famous fractal, the Sierpinski Triangle, and stores the drawing in a picture.

Program

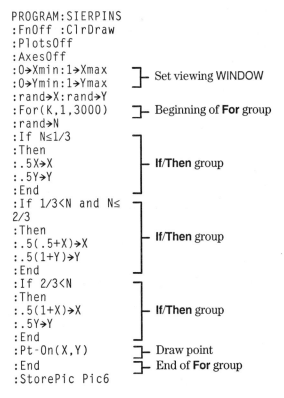

```
PROGRAM:SIERPINS
:FnOff :ClrDraw
:PlotsOff
:AxesOff
:0→Xmin:1→Xmax          ⎤— Set viewing WINDOW
:0→Ymin:1→Ymax          ⎦
:rand→X:rand→Y
:For(K,1,3000)          ⎤— Beginning of For group
:rand→N
:If N≤1/3               ⎤
:Then                   │
:.5X→X                  ├— If/Then group
:.5Y→Y                  │
:End                    ⎦
:If 1/3<N and N≤        ⎤
2/3                     │
:Then                   ├— If/Then group
:.5(.5+X)→X             │
:.5(1+Y)→Y              │
:End                    ⎦
:If 2/3<N               ⎤
:Then                   │
:.5(1+X)→X              ├— If/Then group
:.5Y→Y                  │
:End                    ⎦
:Pt-On(X,Y)             ⎤— Draw point
:End                    ⎤— End of For group
:StorePic Pic6
```

Note: After executing this program, you can recall and display the picture with the instruction **RecallPic Pic6**.

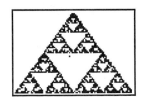

Cobweb Attractors

Using Web WINDOW FORMAT, you can identify points with attracting and repelling behavior in sequence graphing.

Procedure

1. Press MODE. Select **Seq**. Press WINDOW ▶. Select **Web** FORMAT and the defaults. Press 2nd [STAT PLOT] and turn off all stat plots.

2. Press Y=. Enter the sequence. (**Un-$_1$** is on the keyboard.)

   Un=K Un-$_1$ (1−Un-$_1$)

3. Press 2nd [QUIT] to return to the Home screen and store **2.9** to **K**.

4. Press WINDOW. Set the WINDOW variables.

UnStart = .01	Xmin = 0	Ymin = 0
VnStart = 0	Xmax = 1	Ymax = 1
nStart = 0	Xscl = 1	Yscl = 1
nMin = 0		
nMax = 10		

5. Press TRACE to display the graph, and then press ▶ to trace the cobweb. This is a cobweb with one attractor.

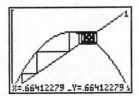

6. Change **K** to **3.44** and TRACE to show a cobweb with two attractors.

7. Change **K** to **3.54** and TRACE to show a cobweb with four attractors.

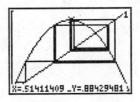

Program: Guess the Coefficients

This program graphs the function A sin BX with random integer coefficients between 1 and 10. You then try to guess the coefficients and graph your guess as C sin DX. The program continues until your guess is correct.

Program

```
PROGRAM:GUESS
:PlotsOff :Func
:FnOff :Radian
:ClrHome
:"Asin BX"→Y₁
:"Csin DX"→Y₂          ⎤— Define equations
:iPart 10rand+1→
A
:iPart 10rand+1→       ⎤— Initialize coefficients
B
:0→C:0→D
:-2π→Xmin
:2π→Xmax
:π/2→Xscl
:-10→Ymin              ⎤— Set viewing WINDOW
:10→Ymax
:1→Yscl
:DispGraph             ⎤— Display graph
:Lbl Z
:Prompt C,D            ⎤— Prompt for guess
:If C=A
:Text(1,1,"C IS
OK")
:If C≠A
:Text(1,1,"C IS
WRONG")
:If D=B
:Text(1,50,"D IS       ⎤— Display results
 OK")
:If D≠B
:Text(1,50,"D IS
 WRONG")
:DispGraph
:Pause
:If C=A and D=B        ⎤— Quit if guesses are correct
:Stop
:Goto Z
```

The Unit Circle and Trigonometric Curves

You can use the parametric graphing feature of the TI-82 to show the relationship between the unit circle and any trigonometric curve.

Problem

Graph the unit circle and the sine curve to demonstrate graphically the relationship between them.

Any function that can be plotted in function graphing can be plotted in parametric graphing by defining the **X** component as **T** and the **Y** component as F(**T**).

Solution

1. Press $\boxed{\text{MODE}}$. Select **Radian**, **Par**, and **Simul**.

2. Press $\boxed{\text{WINDOW}}$. Set the viewing WINDOW.

Tmin = 0	Xmin = -2	Ymin = -3
Tmax = 2π	Xmax = 2π	Ymax = 3
Tstep = .1	Xscl = $\pi/2$	Yscl = 1

3. Press $\boxed{\text{Y=}}$. Turn off all selected functions. Enter the expressions to define the unit circle centered at (-1,0).

   X₁T=cos T–1
   Y₁T=sin T

4. Enter the expressions to define the sine curve.

   X₂T=T
   Y₂T=sin T

5. Press $\boxed{\text{TRACE}}$. As the graph is plotting, you may press $\boxed{\text{ENTER}}$ to pause and resume graphing as you watch the sine function "unwrap" from the unit circle.

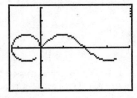

Note: The "unwrapping" can be generalized. Replace **sin T** in **Y₂T** with any other trig function to "unwrap" that function.

Ferris Wheel Problem

Use two pairs of parametric equations to describe two objects in motion, a person on a ferris wheel and a ball thrown to that person. Determine when the two objects are closest.

Problem

The ferris wheel has a diameter of 20 meters (d) and is rotating counterclockwise at a rate of one revolution every 12 seconds (s). The following parametric equation describes the location of the person on the ferris wheel at time T, where α is the angle of rotation, the bottom center of the ferris wheel is (0,0), and the passenger is at the rightmost point (10,10) when T = 0.

$X(T) = r \cos \alpha$ where $\alpha = 2\pi\,T / s$ and $r = d / 2$
$Y(T) = r + r \sin \alpha$

The ball is thrown from a height even with the bottom of the ferris wheel, but 25 meters (b) to the right of the bottom center of the ferris wheel (25,0), with velocity (v_0) of 22 meters per second at an angle (θ) of 66° from the horizontal. The following parametric equation describes the location of the ball at time T.

$X(T) = b - T\,v_0 \cos \theta$
$Y(T) = T\,v_0 \sin \theta - (g/2)\,T^2$ $(g = 9.8\ \text{m/sec}^2)$

Solution

1. Press MODE. Select **Par**, **Connected**, and **Simul**. Simultaneous MODE simulates what is happening with the two objects in motion over time.

2. Press Y= and turn off all functions. Press 2nd [STAT PLOT] and turn off all stat plots.

3. Press WINDOW. Set the viewing WINDOW.

Tmin = 0	Xmin = -13	Ymin = 0
Tmax = 12	Xmax = 34	Ymax = 31
Tstep = .1	Xscl = 10	Yscl = 10

4. Press Y=. Enter the expressions to define the path of the ferris wheel and the path of the ball.

   X₁T=10cos (πT/6)
   Y₁T=10+10sin (πT/6)
   X₂T=25−22Tcos 66°
   Y₂T=22Tsin 66°−(9.8/2)T²

**Solution
(Continued)**

5. Press GRAPH to graph the equations and watch closely as they are plotted. Notice that the ball and the passenger on the ferris wheel appear to be closest near where the paths cross in the upper right quadrant of the ferris wheel.

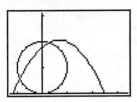

6. Press WINDOW. Change the viewing WINDOW to concentrate on this portion of the graph.

Tmin = 1	Xmin = 0	Ymin = 10
Tmax = 3	Xmax = 23.5	Ymax = 25.5
Tstep = .03	Xscl = 10	Yscl = 10

7. Press TRACE. After the graph is plotted, press ▶ to move near the point on the ferris wheel where the paths cross. Note the values of **X**, **Y**, and **T**.

8. Press ▼ to move to the curve of the ball. Note the values of **X** and **Y** (**T** is unchanged). Notice where the cursor is located. This is the position of the ball when the person on the ferris wheel passes the intersection. Did the ball or the person reach the intersection first?

   Using TRACE, you can, in effect, take "snapshots" in time to explore the relative behavior of two objects in motion.

Reservoir Problem

On the TI-82, parametric graphing can be used to animate a process, providing valuable insight into dynamic problems such as water flow out of a reservoir.

Problem

A new park has a series of waterfalls, fountains, and pools (reservoirs). The height of one of the reservoirs is 2 meters. Several holes of relatively small diameter will be drilled in the side to make streams of water that fall into the next pool.

At what height on the reservoir should a hole be placed to get the maximum distance for the water jet? (Assume that the hole is at x=0, there is no acceleration in the x-direction, and there is no initial velocity in the y-direction.)

Integrating the definition of acceleration in both the x and y directions twice yields the equations $x = v_0 t$ and $y = h_0 - (g/2)t^2$. Solving Bernoulli's equation for v_0 and substituting into $v_0 t$, we get the parametric equations

$$xt = t \sqrt{(2\,g\,(2 - h_0))}$$
$$yt = h_0 - (g/2)\,t^2$$

where t is the time in seconds, h_0 is the height of the hole in the reservoir in meters, and g is the acceleration of gravity (9.8 meters/sec^2).

Procedure

1. Press [MODE]. Select **Par, Simul,** and the defaults.

2. Press [Y=] and [CLEAR] all functions. Enter the equations to plot the water jet for a hole at height **0.5** meters.

   X₁T=T√(2∗9.8(2−0.50))
   Y₁T=0.50−(9.8/2)T²

3. Press [ENTER] to move to **X₂T**. Press [2nd] [RCL] [2nd] [Y-VARS] **2** (to display the **Parametric...** menu) **1** (to select **X₁T**) [ENTER]. This recalls the contents of **X₁T** into **X₂T**. Change the height from **0.50** to **0.75** meters. Repeat the process to recall **Y₁T** into **Y₂T** and edit it.

Procedure (Continued)

4. Repeat step 3 to create three more pairs of equations using the heights **1.00**, **1.50**, and **1.75** meters.

5. Press [WINDOW]. Set the viewing WINDOW.

Tmin = 0	Xmin = 0	Ymin = 0
Tmax = $\sqrt{(4/9.8)}$	Xmax = 2	Ymax = 2
Tstep = .01	Xscl = .5	Yscl = .5

6. Press [ZOOM] and select **ZSquare**. **ZSquare** adjusts the WINDOW variables to include the viewing WINDOW you specified, while providing a realistic (proportional) visual representation of the water jets. It then graphs the trajectories of the water jets from the 5 chosen heights. What height seems to provide the maximum distance for the water jet?

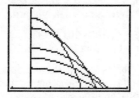

7. Use TRACE to determine the distance from the reservoir where each water jet hits the next pool.

8. Where would you place the holes to construct a fountain that you find visually interesting?

9. Can you think of a way to construct the problem to show two levels of fountains?

Predator-Prey Model

Use sequence graphing on the TI-82 to explore the well-known predator-prey model in biology. Determine the numbers of rabbits and wolves that maintain population equilibrium in a certain region.

Problem

R = Number of rabbits.
M = Growth rate of rabbits if there are no wolves.
K = Rate at which wolves can kill rabbits.
W = Number of wolves.
G = Growth rate of wolves if there are rabbits.
D = Death rate of wolves if there are no rabbits.

$R_n = R_{n-1} (1 + M - K W_{n-1})$
$W_n = W_{n-1} (1 + G R_{n-1} - D)$

Procedure

1. Press $\boxed{\text{MODE}}$. Select **Seq** and the defaults. Press $\boxed{\text{WINDOW}}$ $\boxed{\triangleright}$. Select **Time** FORMAT and the defaults. Press $\boxed{\text{2nd}}$ [STAT PLOT] and turn off all stat plots.

2. Press $\boxed{\text{Y=}}$. Enter functions to describe the number of rabbits (**U**n) and the number of wolves (**V**n) for **M = .05, K = .001, G = .0002, D = .03**. (**V**n-1 and **U**n-1 are 2nd operations on the keyboard.)

   Un=**U**n-1(1+.05−.001 **V**n-1)
   Vn=**V**n-1(1+.0002 **U**n-1−.03)

3. Press $\boxed{\text{WINDOW}}$ and set the initial population of rabbits (**200**) and wolves (**50**), the number of time periods to plot (**400**), and the size of the viewing WINDOW.

UnStart = 200	Xmin = 0	Ymin = 0
VnStart = 50	Xmax = 400	Ymax = 300
nStart = 0	Xscl = 100	Yscl = 100
nMin = 0		
nMax = 400		

4. Press $\boxed{\text{TRACE}}$ to plot and explore the number of rabbits (**U**n) and wolves (**V**n) over time (**n**). Determine the maximum and minimum number of each.

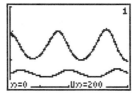

Procedure (Continued)

5. Enter the program:

```
PROGRAM:ORBIT
:ClrDraw:FnOff
:PlotsOff :Dot
:Un(1,99,1)→L1
:Vn(1,99,1)→L2
:Un(100,198,1)→L3
:Vn(100,198,1)→L4
:Un(199,297,1)→L5
:Vn(199,297,1)→L6
:min(L1)-10→Xmin
:max(L1)+10→Xmax
:10→Xscl
:min(L2)-10→Ymin
:max(L2)+10→Ymax
:10→Yscl
:For(I,1,99)
:Pt-On(L1(I),L2(I))
:End
:For(I,1,99)
:Pt-On(L3(I),L4(I))
:End
:For(I,1,99)
:Pt-On(L5(I),L6(I))
:End
```

6. Execute **prgmORBIT**, which shows the cycle of the numbers of rabbits (X axis) and wolves (Y axis) over 297 periods. Use the free-moving cursor to explore the number of rabbits and wolves.

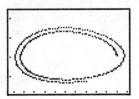

Fundamental Theorem of Calculus

The TI-82 can graph functions that are defined by integrals or derivatives, using the functions fnInt(and nDeriv(from the MATH MATH menu.

Problem 1

Demonstrate graphically that

$$F(x) = \int_1^x 1/t \, dt = \ln(x), \, x>0 \text{ and that}$$

$$D_x \left[\int_1^x 1/t \, dt \right] = 1/x$$

Procedure 1

1. Press MODE. Select **Simul** and the default MODE settings. Press Y= and turn off all functions. Press 2nd [STAT PLOT] and turn off all stat plots.

2. Press WINDOW. Set the viewing WINDOW.

Xmin = .01	Ymin = -1.5
Xmax = 10	Ymax = 2.5
Xscl = 1	Yscl = 1

3. Press Y=. Enter the numerical integral of 1/T and the mathematical integral of 1/X.

   Y₁=fnInt(1/T,T,1,X)
   Y₂=ln X

4. Press TRACE. The busy indicator displays while the graph is being plotted. Use the cursor keys to compare the values of **Y₁** and **Y₂**.

5. Press Y=. Turn off **Y₁** and **Y₂**, and then enter the numerical derivative of the integral of 1/X and the function 1/X.

   Y₃=nDeriv(Y₁,X,X)
   Y₄=1/X

6. Press TRACE. The busy indicator displays while the graph is being plotted. Again, use the cursor keys to compare the values of the two graphed functions, **Y₃** and **Y₄.**

Problem 2

Explore the functions defined by

$$y = \int_{-2}^{x} t^2 \, dt, \int_{0}^{x} t^2 \, dt, \text{ and } \int_{2}^{x} t^2 \, dt$$

Procedure 2

1. Press Y=. Turn off all functions. On the TI-82, the three functions above can be defined simultaneously using a list.

    Y5=fnInt(T², T, {-2,0,2}, X)

2. Press MODE. Select **Sequential**.

3. Press ZOOM **6** to select **ZStandard**.

4. Press TRACE. Notice that the functions appear identical, but shifted vertically by a constant.

5. Press Y=. Enter the numerical derivative of **Y5**.

    Y6=nDeriv(Y5, X, X)

6. Press TRACE. Notice that although the three graphs defined by **Y5** are unique, they share the same derivative.

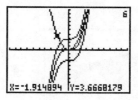

Finding the Area between Curves

Find the area of the region bounded by
f(x) = 300 x / (x² + 625)
g(x) = 3 cos .1 x
x = 75

Procedure

1. Press [MODE]. Select the default MODE settings. Press [Y=] and turn off all functions. Press [2nd] [STAT PLOT] and turn off all stat plots.

2. Press [WINDOW]. Set the viewing WINDOW.

Xmin = 0	Ymin = -5
Xmax = 100	Ymax = 10
Xscl = 10	Yscl = 1

3. Press [Y=]. Enter the upper and lower functions.

   Y₁=300X/(X²+625)
   Y₂=3cos .1X

4. Press [2nd] [CALC] and select **intersection**. The graph is displayed. Select First curve, Second curve, and Guess for the intersection at the left of the display. The solution is displayed, and the value of **X** at the intersection, which is the lower limit of the integral, is stored in **Ans** and **X**.

5. Press [2nd] [DRAW] and use **Shade(** to see the area graphically.

   Shade(Y₂,Y₁,1,Ans,75)

   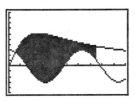

6. Press [2nd] [QUIT] to return to the Home screen. Enter the expression to evaluate the integral for the shaded region.

   fnInt(Y₁−Y₂,X,Ans,75)

   The area is **325.839962**.

Chapter 15: Memory Management

This chapter describes how to manage memory on the TI-82. To increase the amount of memory available for use, occasionally you may want to delete from memory items that you are no longer using. You also can reset the calculator, erasing all data and programs.

Checking Available Memory

The MEMORY Check RAM screen displays the total amount of available memory and the amount of memory used by each variable type. This allows you to determine the amount of memory available for new items such as programs and the amount used by old items that you no longer need.

Displaying the MEM FREE Screen

1. Press [2nd] [MEM] to display the MEMORY screen.

2. Select **Check RAM....**

```
MEM FREE 28734
Real          15
List           0
Matrix         0
Y-Vars       240
Prgm          14
Pic            0
GDB            0
```

The number of bytes used by each variable type is shown on the right.

3. To leave the Check RAM display:

   • To go to the Home screen, press [2nd] [QUIT].

   • To return to the MEMORY screen, press [2nd] [MEM].

Deleting Items from Memory

You can delete the contents of any variable (real number, list, matrix, Y= function), program, picture, or graph database from memory to increase available memory.

Deleting an Item

1. Press [2nd] [MEM] to display the MEMORY screen.

2. Select **Delete....**

3. Select the type of item that you want to delete. (If you select **All...**, a list of all items is displayed.) A screen appears listing all variables of that type and the amount used by each.

   For example, if you select **List...**, the DELETE:List screen appears.

```
DELETE:List
▶L₁            98
 L₂            98
```

4. Use [▲] and [▼] to position the cursor, which is indicated by ▶ in the left column, next to the item you want to delete, and press [ENTER]. The item is deleted immediately.

You can continue to delete individual items from this screen. To leave the DELETE display:

- To go to the Home screen, press [2nd] [QUIT].

- To return to the MEMORY screen, press [2nd] [MEM].

Note: Some system variables can't be deleted; for example, **Ans** and statistical variables such **RegEQ**.

Resetting the TI-82

Resetting the TI-82 restores memory to the factory settings, including deleting the contents of all variables and programs and resetting all system variables to the original settings. Because you can increase available memory by deleting individual items, you should rarely need to reset the TI-82.

Resetting

1. Press [2nd] [MEM] to display the MEMORY screen.

2. Select **Reset....**

3. Make the appropriate menu selection:

   - To go to the Home screen without resetting memory, select **No**.

   - To reset memory, select **Yes**. The Home screen is displayed with the message Mem cleared.

Note: Reset resets the contrast to the factory setting. If the screen is blank, you need to adjust the display contrast. Press [2nd] and then press and hold [▲] (to make the display darker) or [▼] (to make the display lighter). You can press [CLEAR] to clear the message on the display.

Chapter 16: Communication Link

The TI-82 has a port to let you communicate with another TI-82 or with a PC or Macintosh®. This chapter describes how to communicate with another TI-82.

Chapter Contents

Getting Started: Sending Variables

Getting Started is a fast-paced introduction. Read the chapter for details.

Create and store a variable and a random matrix and then transfer them to another TI-82.

1. On the Home screen, press **5** ÷ **3** STO▸ ALPHA **Q** ENTER.

2. Press MATRX ▶ **6** (to select **randM()**). Press **3** , **3**) STO▸ MATRX **1** (to select [**A**]) ENTER to store a random matrix into [**A**].

3. Connect the calculators together with the cable.

4. On the receiving unit, press 2nd [LINK] ▶ to display the RECEIVE menu. Press **1** (to select **Receive**). The message Waiting... is displayed.

5. On the sending unit, press 2nd [LINK] to display the SEND menu. Press **2** to select **SelectAll–** and display the SELECT screen with no items selected.

6. Press ▼ until the cursor is on the line with [**A**]. Press ENTER. The square dot indicates that [**A**] is selected to send.

7. Press ▼ until the cursor is on the line with **Q**. Press ENTER to select **Q** also.

8. On the sending unit, press ▶ to place the cursor on TRANSMIT.

9. Press **1** (to select **Transmit**) and begin transmission. The items are transmitted and both units display the names and types of the transmitted variables.

The TI-82 communication capability lets you share variables and programs or entire memory backup with another TI-82 or with a personal computer. You can print TI-82 screens on a printer connected to a computer.

Linking to Another TI-82

The software for one TI-82 to communicate with another is built into the TI-82. The instructions are in this chapter.

The cable to link the calculators comes with the TI-82.

Note: You cannot transmit items between the TI-82 and other TI graphing calculators such as the TI-85.

Linking to a PC or Macintosh

An optional accessory, TI-GRAPH LINK™, allows a TI-82 to communicate with a personal computer. To obtain the special cable, computer software (for either an IBM®-compatible computer or a Macintosh®), and the instruction booklet, contact Texas Instruments Consumer Relations at 1-800-842-2737 (1-800-TI-CARES).

Connecting the Cable

The TI-82 LINK port is located at the center of the bottom edge of the calculator.

1. Insert either end of the cable into the port **very firmly**.

2. Repeat with the other TI-82.

Leaving a LINK Screen or Menu

To leave LINK:

•   While transmitting, press [ON] to interrupt and then **Quit** to leave the ERROR screen.

•   After transmitting, press [2nd] [QUIT].

Selecting Items

You can send individual items (variables), all items, or a memory backup from one TI-82 to another. To transmit from the TI-82, you first select what you want to send. The transmission does not begin until you select from the TRANSMIT menu.

What You Can Send

You may transmit:

- Programs
- Graph databases
- Pictures
- Lists
- Matrices
- Y= functions
- Window settings (sent as a group)
- RclWindow settings (sent as a group)
- Table settings (sent as a group)
- Real variables

Selecting Items to Send

1. Press [2nd] [LINK] to display the LINK SEND menu.

2. For convenience, you can display the individual items with all of them selected, none of them selected, or the ones from the last transmission selected.

   • **SelectAll+** displays with all items selected.

   • **SelectAll–** displays with no items selected.

   • **SelectCurrent** reselects all currently selected items (page 16–6).

   The SELECT screen is displayed where you may continue to select or deselect individual items. Selected names are marked with a ■.

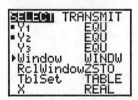

3. ▶ at the left of an item indicates the selection cursor. Use [▼] and [▲] to move the cursor.

   Press [ENTER] to reverse the selection status of the item where the cursor is located.

Transmitting Items

Once you have selected what to send and the receiving
unit is ready, you can begin transmitting. For easy
distribution of items to several TI-82 units, current items
remain selected in both the sending and receiving unit. It
is easy to transmit the items again.

**Transmitting
Items**

After you have selected the items you want to send, press
▶ to move the cursor to TRANSMIT and display the
TRANSMIT menu.

```
SELECT TRANSMIT
1▪Transmit
```

Be sure that the receiving unit is set to Receive
(page 16-7). Press ENTER to select **Transmit**.

The name and type of each item is displayed, one per line,
as the TI-82 tries to transmit it. After transmission is
complete for all items, Done is displayed. Press ▲ and ▼
to scroll through the names.

**Transmitting
Items to an
Additional TI-82**

After sending or receiving data, you can repeat the same
transmission to a different TI-82 from either the sending
unit or the receiving unit without selecting what to send.
The current items remain selected.

Before you make another selection, simply connect the
unit to another TI-82, select **Receive** on the new unit, and
then press 2nd [LINK] **3** (to select **SelectCurrent...**) ▶ **1**
(to select **Transmit**).

**Error
Conditions**

A transmission error occurs after one or two seconds if:

• There is not a cable attached to the sending unit.

• There is not a receiving unit attached to the cable.

• The receiving unit is not in Receive mode.

Note: If the cable is attached, push it in more firmly and
try again.

If the ON key is pressed to interrupt transmission, an
ERROR screen is displayed. Select **Exit** to leave the
ERROR screen.

Receiving Items

Items are not transmitted until the receiving unit is ready. If the receiving unit already has a variable with that name, you have the opportunity to overwrite it, skip it, or save it to a new name.

Receiving Unit

When you select **Receive** from the LINK RECEIVE menu, the busy indicator and the message Waiting... is displayed and the receiving unit is ready to receive transmitted items.

The receiving unit displays the name and type of each item as it is accepted. After transmission is complete for all items, the message Done is displayed. Press ▲ and ▼ to scroll through the names. The unit is not in Receive mode; select **Receive** to receive new items.

To leave Receive mode without receiving items, press [ON]. Select **Quit** to leave the ERROR screen.

Duplicate Name

If an item of that name exists in the receiving unit, the receiving unit displays the DuplicateName menu.

• To store the item to a different name, select **Rename**. After the Name= on the prompt line, enter a variable name that is not being used in the receiving unit (the keyboard is in ALPHA-LOCK). Press [ENTER]. Transmission resumes.

• To overwrite the existing item, select **Overwrite**. Transmission resumes.

• To skip this item (not copy it to the receiving unit), select **Omit**. Transmission resumes with the next item.

• To leave Receive mode, select **Quit**.

Insufficient Memory in Receiving Unit

If the receiving unit does not have sufficient memory to receive the item, the receiving unit displays the Memory Full menu.

• To skip this item, select **Omit**. Transmission resumes with the next item.

• To leave Receive mode, select **Quit**.

Backing Up Memory

Backup transmits all items in memory to the receiving unit.

Memory Backup

To copy the exact contents of memory in the sending unit to the memory of the receiving unit, put the other unit in Receive mode and select **Backup** from the LINK menu.

- Select **Transmit** to begin transmission.

- **Warning:** Backup overwrites the memory in the receiving unit and all information in the memory of the receiving unit is lost. If you do not want to do a backup, select **Quit** to return to the LINK menu.

Receiving Unit

As a safety check to prevent accidental loss of memory, when the receiving unit receives notice of a backup, the message WARNING Memory Backup is displayed.

- To continue with the backup process, select **Continue**. The transmission will begin.

- To prevent the backup, select **Quit**.

Note: If a transmission error occurs during a backup, the receiving unit is reset.

Appendix A: Tables

This appendix provides a list of all TI-82 functions that you can use in expressions and instructions that you can use on the Home screen and in programs.

Table of Functions and Instructions

Functions (F) return a value, list, or matrix and can be used in an expression; instructions (I) initiate an action. Some, but not all, have arguments. † indicates that the instruction is available only in the program editor.

abs *value*	Returns absolute value of *value*. **(F)**	[2nd] [ABS]	2-4
abs *list*	Returns absolute value of *list* elements. **(F)**	[2nd] [ABS]	2-4
abs *matrix*	Returns matrix of absolute values of *matrix* elements. **(F)**	[2nd] [ABS]	10-10
Addition: *valueA+valueB*	Returns *valueA* plus *valueB*. **(F)**	+	2-3
Addition: *value+list*	Returns list in which *value* is added to each *list* element. **(F)**	+	2-3
Addition: *listA+listB*	Returns *listA* elements plus *listB* elements. **(F)**	+	2-3
Addition: *matrixA+matrixB*	Returns *matrixA* elements plus *matrixB* elements. **(F)**	+	10-10
valueA **and** *valueB*	Returns 1 if both *valueA* and *valueB* are ≠ 0. **(F)**	[2nd] [TEST] LOGIC 〈and〉	2-16
augment(*matrixA,matrixB***)**	Returns *matrixA* augmented by *matrixB*. **(F)**	[MATRX] MATH 〈augment(〉	10-14
AxesOff	Sets axis FORMAT off. **(I)**	† [WINDOW] FORMAT 〈AxesOff〉	3-10
AxesOn	Sets axis FORMAT on. **(I)**	† [WINDOW] FORMAT 〈AxesOn〉	3-10
Circle(*X,Y,radius***)**	Draws a circle of center (*X,Y*) and *radius*. **(I)**	[2nd] [DRAW] DRAW 〈Circle(〉	8-9
ClrDraw	Deletes all drawn elements from a graph or drawing. **(I)**	[2nd] [DRAW] DRAW 〈ClrDraw〉	8-16

ClrHome	Clears the Home screen. (I)	† PRGM I/O 〈ClrHome〉	13-17
ClrList *listA,listB,* . . .	Clears all values from *listA, listB,* . . . (I)	STAT EDIT 〈ClrList〉	12-12
ClrTable	Clears all values from table. (I)	† PRGM I/O 〈ClrTable〉	13-17
Connected	Sets connected line graphing format. (I)	† MODE 〈Connected〉	1-11
CoordOff	Does not display cursor coordinate values. (I)	† WINDOW FORMAT 〈CoordOff〉	3-10
CoordOn	Displays cursor coordinate values. (I)	† WINDOW FORMAT 〈CoordOn〉	3-10
cos *value*	Returns cosine of *value*. (F)	COS	2-3
cos *list*	Returns cosine of *list* elements. (F)	COS	2-3
cos⁻¹ *value*	Returns arccosine of *value*. (F)	2nd [cos⁻¹]	2-3
cos⁻¹ *list*	Returns arccosine of *list* elements. (F)	2nd [cos⁻¹]	2-3
cosh *value*	Returns hyperbolic cosine of *value*. (F)	MATH HYP 〈cosh〉	2-11
cosh *list*	Returns hyperbolic cosine of *list* elements. (F)	MATH HYP 〈cosh〉	2-11
cosh⁻¹ *value*	Returns hyperbolic arccosine of *value*. (F)	MATH HYP 〈cosh⁻¹〉	2-11
cosh⁻¹ *list*	Returns hyperbolic arccosine of *list* elements. (F)	MATH HYP 〈cosh⁻¹〉	2-11
Cube: *value*³	Returns cube of *value*. (F)	MATH MATH 〈³〉	2-6
Cube: *list*³	Returns cube of *list* elements. (F)	MATH MATH 〈³〉	2-6
Cube: *matrix*³	Returns *matrix* cubed. (I)	MATH MATH 〈³〉	10-11
Cube root: ³√*value*	Returns cube root of *value*. (F)	MATH MATH 〈³√〉	2-6
Cube root: ³√*list*	Returns cube root of *list* elements. (F)	MATH MATH 〈³√〉	2-6

Table of Functions and Instructions (Continued)

CubicReg	Fits data to cubic model using lists from SET UP CALCS. (I)	STAT CALC ⟨CubicReg⟩ 12-15
CubicReg *Xlist*,*Ylist*	Fits *Xlist* and *Ylist* to cubic model. (I)	STAT CALC ⟨CubicReg⟩ 12-15
CubicReg *Xlist*,*Ylist*,*Flist*	Fits *Xlist* and *Ylist* to cubic model with frequency *Flist*. (I)	STAT CALC ⟨CubicReg⟩ 12-15
value▶**Dec**	Displays *value* as decimal. (I)	MATH MATH ⟨▶Dec⟩ 2-5
list▶**Dec**	Displays *list* as decimal. (I)	MATH MATH ⟨▶Dec⟩ 2-5
matrix▶**Dec**	Displays *matrix* as decimal. (I)	MATH MATH ⟨▶Dec⟩ 2-5
Degree	Sets degree MODE. (I)	† MODE ⟨Degree⟩ 1-11
Degree notation: *angle°*	Interprets *angle* as degrees. (F)	2nd [ANGLE] ⟨°⟩ 2-13
DependAsk	Sets table without dependent variables. (I)	† PRGM 2nd [TblSet] ⟨DependAsk⟩ 7-5
DependAuto	Sets table to generate dependent variables. (I)	† PRGM 2nd [TblSet] ⟨DependAuto⟩ 7-5
det *matrix*	Returns determinant of *matrix*. (F)	MATRX MATH ⟨det⟩ 10-12
dim *list*	Returns length of *list*. (F)	2nd [LIST] OPS ⟨dim⟩ 11-7
dim *matrix*	Returns dimensions of *matrix* as a list. (F)	MATRX MATH ⟨dim⟩ 10-12,13
length➔**dim** *listname*	Creates (if necessary) or redimensions *list* to *length*. (I)	2nd [LIST] OPS ⟨dim⟩ 11-7
{*row*,*col*}➔**dim** *matrixname*	Creates (if necessary) or redimensions *matrix* to *row* × *col*. (I)	MATRX MATH ⟨dim⟩ 10-13
Disp	Displays Home screen. (I)	† PRGM I/O ⟨Disp⟩ 13-14
Disp *valueA*,*valueB*, . . .	Displays *valueA*, *valueB*, . . . (I)	† PRGM I/O ⟨Disp⟩ 13-14
DispGraph	Displays graph. (I)	† PRGM I/O ⟨DispGraph⟩ 13-15
DispTable	Displays table. (I)	† PRGM I/O ⟨DispTable⟩ 13-15

Division: *valueA/valueB*	Returns *valueA* divided by *valueB*. **(F)**	÷	2-3
Division: *list/value*	Returns *list* elements divided by *value*. **(F)**	÷	2-3
Division: *value/list*	Returns *value* divided by *list* elements. **(F)**	÷	2-3
Division: *listA/listB*	Returns *listA* elements divided by *listB* elements. **(F)**	÷	2-3
answer▶**DMS**	Displays *answer* in DMS format. **(I)**	[2nd] [ANGLE] ⟨▶DMS⟩	2-14
Dot	Sets dot graphing format. **(I)**	† [MODE] ⟨Dot⟩	1-11
DrawF *expression*	Draws *expression* (in **X**) on current graph. **(I)**	[2nd] [DRAW] DRAW ⟨DrawF⟩	8-7
DrawInv *expression*	Draws inverse of *expression* (in **X**) on current **Func** MODE graph. **(I)**	[2nd] [DRAW] DRAW ⟨DrawInv⟩	8-7
DS<(*variable,value*) :*commandA* :*commands*	Decrements *variable* by 1, skips *commandA* if *variable<value*. **(I)**	† [PRGM] CTL ⟨DS<(⟩	13-10
e^*power*	Returns **e** raised to *power*. **(F)**	[2nd] [e^x]	2-4
e^*list*	Returns a list of **e** raised to *list* elements. **(F)**	[2nd] [e^x]	2-4
Else *See* **If:Then:Else**			
End	Indentifies end of **While**, **For**, **Repeat**, or **If-Then-Else** loop. **(I)**	† [PRGM] CTL ⟨End⟩	13-9
Eng	Sets engineering display MODE. **(I)**	† [MODE] ⟨Eng⟩	1-10
Equal: *valueA=valueB*	Returns 1 if *valueA* = *valueB*. Returns 0 if *valueA* ≠ *valueB*. **(F)**	[2nd] [TEST] TEST ⟨=⟩	2-15
Equal: *listA=listB*	Returns 1 if every element of *listA* = *listB*. Returns 0 if any element of *listA* ≠ *listB*. **(F)**	[2nd] [TEST] TEST ⟨=⟩	2-15
Equal: *matrixA=matrixB*	Returns 1 if every element of *matrixA* = *matrixB*. Returns 0 if any element of *matrixA* ≠ *matrixB*. **(F)**	[2nd] [TEST] TEST ⟨=⟩	10-11

Table of Functions and Instructions (Continued)

Exponent: *valueEexponent*	Returns *value* times 10 to the *exponent*. (F)	[2nd] [EE]	1-7
Exponent: *listEexponent*	Returns *list* elements time 10 to the *exponent*. (F)	[2nd] [EE]	1-7
Exponent: *matrixEexponent*	Returns *matrix* elements times 10 to the *exponent*. (F)	[2nd] [EE]	1-7
ExpReg	Fits data to exponential model using lists from SET UP CALCS. (I)	[STAT] CALC ⟨ExpReg⟩	12-16
ExpReg *Xlist,Ylist*	Fits *Xlist* and *Ylist* to exponential model. (I)	[STAT] CALC ⟨ExpReg⟩	12-16
ExpReg *Xlist,Ylist,Flist*	Fits *Xlist* and *Ylist* to exponential model with frequency *Flist*.(I)	[STAT] CALC ⟨ExpReg⟩	12-16
Factorial: *value*!	Returns factorial of *value* (0≤integer≤69). (F)	[MATH] PRB ⟨!⟩	2-12
Factorial: *list*!	Returns factorial of *list* elements. (F)	[MATH] PRB ⟨!⟩	2-12
Fill(*value,matrixname***)**	Stores *value* to each element in *matrixname*. (I)	[MATRX] MATH ⟨Fill(⟩	10-13
Fill(*value,listname***)**	Stores *value* to each element in *listname*. (I)	[2nd] [LIST] OPS ⟨Fill(⟩	11-8
Fix #	Sets fixed display MODE for # decimal places. (I)	† [MODE] ⟨#⟩	1-10
Float	Sets floating display MODE. (I)	† [MODE] ⟨Float⟩	1-10
fMax(*expression,variable, lower,upper***)**	Returns value of *variable* where maximum of *expression* occurs, between *lower* and *upper*. Tolerance is 1E-5. (F)	[MATH] MATH ⟨fMax(⟩	2-6
fMax(*expression,variable, lower,upper,tolerance***)**	Returns value of *variable* where maximum of *expression* occurs, between *lower* and *upper*, with specified *tolerance*. (F)	[MATH] MATH ⟨fMax(⟩	2-6

fMin(_expression,variable,_ _lower,upper_**)**	Returns value of _variable_ where minimum of _expression_ occurs, between _lower_ and _upper_. Tolerance is 1E-5. **(F)**	MATH MATH ⟨fMin()⟩ 2-6
fMin(_expression,variable,_ _lower,upper,tolerance_**)**	Returns value of _variable_ where minimum of _expression_ occurs, between _lower_ and _upper_, with specified _tolerance_. **(F)**	MATH MATH ⟨fMin()⟩ 2-6
fnInt(_expression,variable,_ _lower,upper_**)**	Returns function integral of _expression_ with respect to _variable_, between _lower_ and _upper_. Tolerance is 1E-5. **(F)**	MATH MATH ⟨fnInt()⟩ 2-7
fnInt(_expression,variable,_ _lower,upper,tolerance_**)**	Returns function integral of _expression_ with respect to _variable_, between _lower_ and _upper_, with specified _tolerance_. **(F)**	MATH MATH ⟨fnInt()⟩ 2-7
FnOff	Deselects all Y= functions. **(I)**	2nd [Y-VARS] ON/OFF ⟨FnOff⟩ 3-7
FnOff _funcA,funcB, . . ._	Deselects _funcA, funcB,_ . . . **(I)**	2nd [Y-VARS] ON/OFF ⟨FnOff⟩ 3-7
FnOn	Selects all Y= functions. **(I)**	2nd [Y-VARS] ON/OFF ⟨FnOn⟩ 3-7
FnOn _funcA,funcB, . . ._	Selects _funcA, funcB,_ . . . **(I)**	2nd [Y-VARS] ON/OFF ⟨FnOn⟩ 3-7
For(_variable,begin,end_**)** :_commands_ . . . :**End**	Executes _commands_ through **End**, incrementing _variable_ from _begin_ by 1 until _variable>end._ **(I)**	† PRGM CTL ⟨For()⟩ 13-8
For(_variable,begin,end,_ _increment_**)** :_commands_ . . . :**End**	Executes _commands_ through **End**, incrementing _variable_ from _begin_ by _increment_ until _variable>end._ **(I)**	† PRGM CTL ⟨For()⟩ 13-8
fPart _value_	Returns fractional part of _value._ **(F)**	MATH NUM ⟨fPart⟩ 2-9
fPart _list_	Returns fractional part of each _list_ element. **(F)**	MATH NUM ⟨fPart⟩ 2-9

Table of Functions and Instructions (Continued)

fPart *matrix*	Returns fractional part of each *matrix* element. **(F)**	[MATH] NUM ⟨fPart⟩ 10-11
value▶**Frac**	Displays *value* as most simplified fraction. **(I)**	[MATH] MATH ⟨▶Frac⟩ 2-5
list▶**Frac**	Displays *list* elements as most simplified fractions. **(I)**	[MATH] MATH ⟨▶Frac⟩ 11-2
matrix▶**Frac**	Displays *matrix* elements as most simplified fractions. **(I)**	[MATH] MATH ⟨▶Frac⟩ 2-5
FullScreen	Sets display MODE to show full screen. **(I)**	† [MODE] ⟨FullScreen⟩ 1-11
Func	Sets function graphing MODE. **(I)**	† [MODE] ⟨Func⟩ 1-11
Get(*variable***)**	Gets contents of *variable* from external device and stores in *variable*. **(I)**	† [PRGM] I/O ⟨Get()⟩ 13-17
getKey	Returns value of last keystroke. **(F)**	† [PRGM] I/O ⟨getKey⟩ 13-16
Goto *label*	Transfers control to *label*. **(I)**	† [PRGM] CTL ⟨Goto⟩ 13-10
Greater than: *valueA*>*valueB*	Returns 1 if *valueA* > *valueB*. Returns 0 if *valueA* ≤ *valueB*. **(F)**	[2nd] [TEST] TEST ⟨>⟩ 2-15
Greater than: *listA*>*listB*	Returns 1 if *listA* element > *listB* element. Otherwise returns 0. **(F)**	[2nd] [TEST] TEST ⟨>⟩ 2-15
Greater than or equal: *valueA*≥*valueB*	Returns 1 if *valueA* ≥ *valueB*. Returns 0 if *valueA* < *valueB*. **(F)**	[2nd] [TEST] TEST ⟨≥⟩ 2-15
Greater than or equal: *listA*≥*listB*	Returns 1 if *listA* element ≥ *listB* element. Otherwise returns 0. **(F)**	[2nd] [TEST] TEST ⟨≥⟩ 2-15
GridOff	Sets grid FORMAT off. **(I)**	† [WINDOW] FORMAT ⟨GridOff⟩ 3-10
GridOn	Sets grid FORMAT on. **(I)**	† [WINDOW] FORMAT ⟨GridOn⟩ 3-10
Horizontal *Y*	Draws horizontal line at *Y*. **(I)**	[2nd] [DRAW] DRAW ⟨Horizontal⟩ 8-5
identity *dim*	Returns identity matrix *dim* × *dim*. **(F)**	[MATRX] MATH ⟨identity⟩ 10-13

If *condition*:*commandA* :*commands*	If *condition* = 0 (false), skips *commandA*. **(I)**	† PRGM CTL ⟨If⟩ 13-7
If *condition* :**Then:***commands*:**End**	Executes *commands* from **Then** to **End** if *condition* = 1 (true). **(I)**	† PRGM CTL ⟨Then⟩ 13-8
If *condition* :**Then:***commands* :**Else:***commands*:**End**	Executes *commands* from **Then** to **Else** if *condition* = 1 (true); from **Else** to **End** if *condition* = 0 (false). **(I)**	† PRGM CTL ⟨Else⟩ 13-8
IndpntAsk	Sets table without independent values. **(I)**	† PRGM [2nd] [TblSet] ⟨IndpntAsk⟩ 7-5
IndpntAuto	Sets table to generate independent values. **(I)**	† PRGM [2nd] [TblSet] ⟨IndpntAuto⟩ 7-5
Input	Displays graph. **(I)**	† PRGM I/O ⟨Input⟩ 13-13
Input *variable*	Prompts for value to store to *variable*. **(I)**	† PRGM I/O ⟨Input⟩ 13-13
Input "*string*",*variable*	Displays *string* and stores entered value to *variable*. **(I)**	† PRGM I/O ⟨Input⟩ 13-13
int *value*	Returns largest integer ≤ *value*. **(F)**	[MATH] NUM ⟨int⟩ 2-10
int *list*	Returns largest integer ≤ *list* element. **(F)**	[MATH] NUM ⟨int⟩ 2-10
int *matrix*	Returns matrix of largest integers ≤ each element of *matrix*. **(F)**	[MATH] NUM ⟨int⟩ 10-11
Inverse: *value*⁻¹	Returns 1 divided by *value*. **(F)**	x^{-1} 2-3
Inverse: *list*⁻¹	Returns 1 divided by *list* elements. **(F)**	x^{-1} 2-3
Inverse: *matrix*⁻¹	Returns *matrix* inverted. **(F)**	x^{-1} 10-11
iPart *value*	Returns integer part of *value*. **(F)**	[MATH] NUM ⟨iPart⟩ 2-9
iPart *list*	Returns integer part of *list* element. **(F)**	[MATH] NUM ⟨iPart⟩ 2-9
iPart *matrix*	Returns matrix of integer part of each element of *matrix*. **(F)**	[MATH] NUM ⟨iPart⟩ 10-11
IS>(*variable*,*value*) :*commandA* :*commands*	Increments *variable* by 1, skips *commandA* if *variable*>*value*. **(I)**	† PRGM CTL ⟨IS>()⟩ 13-10

Table of Functions and Instructions (Continued)

LabelOff	Sets axis label FORMAT off. (I)	† [WINDOW] FORMAT ⟨LabelOff⟩ 3-10
LabelOn	Sets axis label FORMAT on. (I)	† [WINDOW] FORMAT ⟨LabelOn⟩ 3-10
Lbl *label*	Assigns *label* to the command. (I)	† [PRGM] CTL ⟨Lbl⟩ 13-10
Less than: *valueA*<*valueB*	Returns 1 if *valueA* < *valueB*. Returns 0 if *valueA* ≥ *valueB*. (F)	[2nd] [TEST] TEST ⟨<⟩ 2-15
Less than: *listA*<*listB*	Returns 1 if *listA* element < *listB* element; otherwise returns 0. (F)	[2nd] [TEST] TEST ⟨<⟩ 2-15
Less than or equal: *valueA*≤*valueB*	Returns 1 if *valueA* ≤ *valueB*. Returns 0 if *valueA* > *valueB*. (F)	[2nd] [TEST] TEST ⟨≤⟩ 2-15
Less than or equal: *listA*≤*listB*	Returns 1 if *listA* element ≤ *listB* element. Otherwise returns 0. (F)	[2nd] [TEST] TEST ⟨≤⟩ 2-15
Line(X_1,Y_1,X_2,Y_2)	Draws line from (X_1,Y_1) to (X_2,Y_2). (I)	[2nd] [DRAW] DRAW ⟨Line(⟩ 8-4
Line(X_1,Y_1,X_2,Y_2,0)	Erases line from (X_1,Y_1) to (X_2,Y_2). (I)	[2nd] [DRAW] DRAW ⟨Line(⟩ 8-4
LinReg(a+bx) **LinReg(ax+b)**	Fits data to linear model using lists from SET UP CALCS. (I)	[STAT] CALC ⟨LinReg(a+bx)⟩ 12-15 ⟨LinReg(ax+b)⟩ 12-16
LinReg(a+bx) *Xlist,Ylist* **LinReg(ax+b)** *Xlist,Ylist*	Fits *Xlist* and *Ylist* to linear model. (I)	[STAT] CALC ⟨LinReg(a+bx)⟩ 12-15 [STAT] CALC ⟨LinReg(ax+b)⟩ 12-16
LinReg(a+bx) *Xlist,Ylist, Flist* **LinReg(ax+b)** *Xlist,Ylist, Flist*	Fits *Xlist* and *Ylist* to linear model with frequency *Flist*. (I)	[STAT] CALC ⟨LinReg(a+bx)⟩ 12-15 [STAT] CALC ⟨LinReg(ax+b)⟩ 12-16
In *value*	Returns natural logarithm of *value*. (F)	[LN] 2-4
In *list*	Returns natural logarithm of *list* elements. (F)	[LN] 2-4
LnReg	Fits data to logarithmic model using lists from SET UP CALCS. (I)	[STAT] CALC ⟨LnReg⟩ 12-16
LnReg *Xlist,Ylist*	Fits *Xlist* and *Ylist* to logarithmic model. (I)	[STAT] CALC ⟨LnReg⟩ 12-16

LnReg *Xlist,Ylist,Flist*	Fits *Xlist* and *Ylist* to logarithmic model with frequency *Flist*. **(I)**	STAT CALC ⟨LnReg⟩ 12–16
log *value*	Returns logarithm of *value*. **(F)**	LOG 2–4
log *list*	Returns logarithm of *list* elements. **(F)**	LOG 2–4
max(*valueA*,*valueB***)**	Returns larger of *valueA* and *valueB*. **(F)**	MATH NUM ⟨max(⟩ 2–10
max(*list***)**	Returns largest element in *list*. **(F)**	2nd [LIST] MATH ⟨max(⟩ 11–9
max(*listA*,*listB***)**	Returns a list of the larger of each pair of elements in *listA* and *listB*. **(F)**	2nd [LIST] MATH ⟨max(⟩ 11–9
mean(*list***)**	Returns the mean of *list*. **(F)**	2nd [LIST] MATH ⟨mean(⟩ 11–9
mean(*list*,*Flist***)**	Returns the mean of *list* with frequency *Flist*. **(F)**	2nd [LIST] MATH ⟨mean(⟩ 11–9
Med-Med	Fits data to median-median model using lists from SET UP CALCS. **(I)**	STAT CALC ⟨Med-Med⟩ 12–15
Med-Med *Xlist,Ylist*	Fits *Xlist* and *Ylist* to median-median model. **(I)**	STAT CALC ⟨Med-Med⟩ 12–15
Med-Med *Xlist,Ylist,Flist*	Fits *Xlist* and *Ylist* to median-median model with frequency *Flist*. **(I)**	STAT CALC ⟨Med-Med⟩ 12–15
median(*list***)**	Returns the median of *list*. **(F)**	2nd [LIST] MATH ⟨median(⟩ 11–9
median(*list*,*Flist***)**	Returns the median of *list* with frequency *Flist*. **(F)**	2nd [LIST] MATH ⟨median(⟩ 11–9
Menu("*title***","***text***",***label*, "***text***",***label*, . . .)**	Sets up branches for up to 7 menu items. **(I)**	† PRGM CTL ⟨Menu(⟩ 13–11
min(*valueA*,*valueB***)**	Returns smaller of *valueA* and *valueB*. **(F)**	MATH NUM ⟨min(⟩ 2–10
min(*list***)**	Returns smallest element in *list*. **(F)**	2nd [LIST] MATH ⟨min(⟩ 11–9
min(*listA*,*listB***)**	Returns list of smaller of each pair of elements in *listA* and *listB*. **(F)**	2nd [LIST] MATH ⟨min(⟩ 11–9

Table of Functions and Instructions (Continued)

Minute notation: *degrees'minutes'seconds'*	Interprets angle as *degrees*, *minutes*, and *seconds*. **(F)**	[2nd] [ANGLE] ⟨'⟩ 2-13
Multiplication: *valueA∗valueB*	Returns *valueA* times *valueB*. **(F)**	[×] 2-3
Multiplication: *value∗list*	Returns *value* times each *list* element. **(F)**	[×] 2-3
Multiplication: *list∗value*	Returns each *list* element times *value*. **(F)**	[×] 2-3
Multiplication: *listA∗listB*	Returns *listA* elements times *listB* elements. **(F)**	[×] 2-3
Multiplication: *value∗matrix*	Returns *value* times *matrix* elements. **(F)**	[×] 10-10
Multiplication: *matrixA∗matrixB*	Returns *matrixA* times *matrixB*. **(F)**	[×] 10-10
items **nCr** *number*	Returns combinations of *items* (integer≥0) taken *number* (integer≥0) at a time. **(F)**	[MATH] PRB ⟨nCr⟩ 2-12
nDeriv(*expression,* *variable,value***)**	Returns approximate numerical derivative of *expression* with respect to *variable* at *value*. ε is 1E-3. **(F)**	[MATH] MATH ⟨nDeriv()⟩ 2-7
nDeriv(*expression,* *variable,value,ε***)**	Returns approximate numerical derivative of *expression* with respect to *variable* at *value*, with specified ε. **(F)**	[MATH] MATH ⟨nDeriv()⟩ 2-7
Negation: *-value*	Returns negative of *value*. **(F)**	[(-)] 2-4
Negation: *-list*	Returns *list* with each element negated. **(F)**	[(-)] 2-4
Negation: *-matrix*	Returns *matrix* with each element negated. **(F)**	[(-)] 10-10

Normal	Sets normal display MODE. **(I)**	† MODE ⟨Normal⟩	1-10
not *value*	Returns 0 if *value* is ≠ 0. **(F)**	2nd [TEST] LOGIC ⟨not⟩	2-16
Not equal: *valueA≠valueB*	Returns 1 if *valueA* ≠ *valueB*. Returns 0 if *valueA = valueB*. **(F)**	2nd [TEST] TEST ⟨≠⟩	2-15
Not equal: *listA≠listB*	Returns 1 if *listA* element ≠ *listB* element. Otherwise, returns 0. **(F)**	2nd [TEST] TEST ⟨≠⟩	2-15
Not equal: *matrixA≠matrixB*	Returns 1 if *matrixA* element ≠ *matrixB* element. Otherwise, returns 0. **(F)**	2nd [TEST] TEST ⟨≠⟩	10-11
items **nPr** *number*	Returns permutations of *items* (0≤integer) taken *number* (0≤integer) at a time. **(F)**	MATH PRB ⟨nPr⟩	2-12
1-Var Stats	Performs one-variable analysis using lists from SET UP CALCS. **(I)**	STAT CALC ⟨1-Var Stats⟩	12-14
1-Var Stats *Xlist*	Performs one-variable analysis using *Xlist* and a frequency of 1. **(I)**	STAT CALC ⟨1-Var Stats⟩	12-14
1-Var Stats *Xlist,Flist*	Performs one-variable analysis using *Xlist* and frequencies from *Ylist*. **(I)**	STAT CALC ⟨1-Var Stats⟩	12-14
valueA **or** *valueB*	Returns 1 if *valueA* or *valueB* is ≠ 0. **(F)**	2nd [TEST] LOGIC ⟨or⟩	2-16
Output(*line,column,*"*text*"**)**	Displays *text* beginning at specified *line* and *column*. **(I)**	† PRGM I/O ⟨Output()⟩	13-15
Output(*line,column,value***)**	Displays *value* beginning at specified *line* and *column*. **(I)**	† PRGM I/O ⟨Output()⟩	13-15

Table of Functions and Instructions (Continued)

Par	Sets parametric graphing MODE. **(I)**	† [MODE] ⟨Par⟩ 1-11
Pause	Suspends program execution until [ENTER] is pressed. **(I)**	† [PRGM] CTL ⟨Pause⟩ 13-10
Pause *value*	Displays *value*, suspends program execution until [ENTER] is pressed. **(I)**	† [PRGM] CTL ⟨Pause⟩ 13-10
Plot#(*type,Xlist,Ylist, mark***)**	Defines **Plot**# (1-3) of *type* **Scatter** or **xyLine** for *Xlist* and *Ylist* using *mark*. **(I)**	† [2nd] [STAT PLOT] ⟨Plot#(⟩ 12-20
Plot#(*type,Xlist,Flist***)**	Defines **Plot**# (1-3) of *type* **Histogram** or **Boxplot** for *Xlist* with frequency *Flist*. **(I)**	† [2nd] [STAT PLOT] ⟨Plot#(⟩ 12-20
PlotsOff	Deselects all stat plots. **(I)**	† [2nd] [STAT PLOT] ⟨PlotsOff⟩ 12-21
PlotsOff *plot#,plot#,* . . .	Deselects stat **Plot1**, **Plot2**, or **Plot3**. **(I)**	† [2nd] [STAT PLOT] ⟨PlotsOff⟩ 12-21
PlotsOn	Selects all stat plots. **(I)**	† [2nd] [STAT PLOT] ⟨PlotsOn⟩ 12-21
PlotsOn *plot#,plot#,* . . .	Selects stat **Plot1, Plot2,** or **Plot3**. **(I)**	† [2nd] [STAT PLOT] ⟨PlotsOn⟩ 12-21
Pol	Sets polar graphing MODE. **(I)**	† [MODE] ⟨Pol⟩ 1-11
PolarGC	Sets polar graphing coordinates. **(I)**	† [WINDOW] FORMAT ⟨PolarGC⟩ 3-10
Power of ten: **10^***value*	Returns 10 raised to *value* power. **(F)**	[2nd] [10^x] 2-4
Power of ten: **10^***list*	Returns list of 10 raised to *list* power. **(F)**	[2nd] [10^x] 2-4
Powers: *value^power*	Returns *value* raised to *power*. **(F)**	[^] 2-3
Powers: *list^power*	Returns *list* elements raised to *power*. **(F)**	[^] 2-3
Powers: *value^list*	Returns *value* raised to *list* elements. **(F)**	[^] 2-3
Powers: *matrix^power*	Returns *matrix* elements raised to *power*. **(F)**	[^] 10-11
prgm*name*	Executes program *name*. **(I)**	[PRGM] CTRL ⟨prgm⟩ 13-11
PrintScreen	Sends current display to printer. **(I)**	† [PRGM] I/O ⟨PrintScreen⟩ 13-17

prod *list*	Returns product of *list* elements. **(F)**	2nd [LIST] MATH ⟨prod⟩ 11-10
Prompt *varA,varB,* ...	Prompts for value for *varA*, then *varB*, etc. **(I)**	† PRGM I/O ⟨Prompt⟩ 13-15
P▸Rx(R,θ)	Returns **X**, given polar coordinates R and θ. **(F)**	2nd [ANGLE] ⟨P▸Rx(⟩ 2-14
P▸Ry(R,θ)	Returns **Y**, given polar coordinates R and θ. **(F)**	2nd [ANGLE] ⟨P▸Ry(⟩ 2-14
Pt-Change(X,Y)	Changes point at (X,Y). **(I)**	2nd [DRAW] POINTS ⟨Pt-Change(⟩ 8-12
Pt-Off(X,Y)	Erases point at (X,Y). **(I)**	2nd [DRAW] POINTS ⟨Pt-Off(⟩ 8-12
Pt-On(X,Y)	Draws point at (X,Y). **(I)**	2nd [DRAW] POINTS ⟨Pt-On(⟩ 8-12
PwrReg	Fits data to power model using lists from SET UP CALCS. **(I)**	STAT CALC ⟨PwrReg⟩ 12-16
PwrReg *Xlist,Ylist*	Fits *Xlist* and *Ylist* to power model. **(I)**	STAT CALC ⟨PwrReg⟩ 12-16
PwrReg *Xlist,Ylist,Flist*	Fits *Xlist* and *Ylist* to power model with frequency *Flist*. **(I)**	STAT CALC ⟨PwrReg⟩ 12-16
Pxl-Change(*row,column*)	Changes pixel at (*row, column*); $0 \le row \le 62$ and $0 \le column \le 94$. **(I)**	2nd [DRAW] POINTS ⟨Pxl-Change(⟩ 8-13
Pxl-Off(*row,column*)	Erases pixel at (*row, column*); $0 \le row \le 62$ and $0 \le column \le 94$. **(I)**	2nd [DRAW] POINTS ⟨Pxl-Off(⟩ 8-13
Pxl-On(*row,column*)	Draws pixel at (*row, column*); $0 \le row \le 62$ and $0 \le column \le 94$. **(I)**	2nd [DRAW] POINTS ⟨Pxl-On(⟩ 8-13
pxl-Test(*row,column*)	Returns 1 if pixel (*row, column*) is on, 0 if it is off; $0 \le row \le 62$ and $0 \le column \le 94$. **(F)**	2nd [DRAW] POINTS ⟨pxl-Test(⟩ 8-13
QuadReg	Fits data to quadratic model using lists from SET UP CALCS. **(I)**	STAT CALC ⟨QuadReg⟩ 12-15
QuadReg *Xlist,Ylist*	Fits *Xlist* and *Ylist* to quadratic model. **(I)**	STAT CALC ⟨QuadReg⟩ 12-15
QuadReg *Xlist,Ylist,Flist*	Fits *Xlist* and *Ylist* to quadratic model with frequency *Flist*. **(I)**	STAT CALC ⟨QuadReg⟩ 12-15

Table of Functions and Instructions (Continued)

QuartReg	Fits data to quartic model using lists from SET UP CALCS. **(I)**	[STAT] CALC ⟨QuartReg⟩ 12-15
QuartReg *Xlist,Ylist*	Fits *Xlist* and *Ylist* to quartic model. **(I)**	[STAT] CALC ⟨QuartReg⟩ 12-15
QuartReg *Xlist,Ylist,Flist*	Fits *Xlist* and *Ylist* to quartic model with frequency *Flist*. **(I)**	[STAT] CALC ⟨QuartReg⟩ 12-15
*angle*ʳ	Interprets *angle* as radians. **(F)**	[2nd] [ANGLE] ⟨ʳ⟩ 2-13
Radian	Sets radian MODE. **(I)**	† [MODE] ⟨Radian⟩ 1-11
rand	Returns random number between 0 and 1. **(F)**	[MATH] PRB ⟨rand⟩ 2-12
randM(*rows,columns***)**	Returns a *rows* (1-99) × *columns* (1-99) random matrix. **(F)**	[MATRX] MATH ⟨randM(⟩ 10-13
RecallGDB GDB*n*	Recalls graph database **GDB***n* as the current graph. **(I)**	[2nd] [DRAW] STO ⟨RecallGDB⟩ 8-15
RecallPic Pic*n*	Recalls picture **Pic***n* onto current graph. **(I)**	[2nd] [DRAW] STO ⟨RecallPic⟩ 8-14
RectGC	Sets rectangular graphing coordinates. **(I)**	† [WINDOW] FORMAT ⟨RectGC⟩ 3-10
Repeat *condition* :*commands*:**End**	Execute *commands* until *condition* is true. **(I)**	† [PRGM] CTL ⟨Repeat⟩ 13-9
Return	Returns to calling program. **(I)**	† [PRGM] CTL ⟨Return⟩ 13-12
n^{th}root$^x\sqrt{}$*value*	Returns n^{th}root of *value*. **(F)**	[MATH] MATH ⟨$^x\sqrt{}$⟩ 2-6
n^{th}root$^x\sqrt{}$*list*	Returns n^{th}root of *list* elements. **(F)**	[MATH] MATH ⟨$^x\sqrt{}$⟩ 2-6
list$^x\sqrt{}$*value*	Returns *list* roots of *value*. **(F)**	[MATH] MATH ⟨$^x\sqrt{}$⟩ 2-6
listA$^x\sqrt{}$*listB*	Returns *list* roots of *list*. **(F)**	[MATH] MATH ⟨$^x\sqrt{}$⟩ 2-6
round(*value***)**	Returns *value* rounded to 10 digits. **(F)**	[MATH] NUM ⟨round(⟩ 2-9
round(*value,#decimals***)**	Returns *value* rounded to #*decimals* (≤9). **(F)**	[MATH] NUM ⟨round(⟩ 2-9
round(*list***)**	Returns *list* elements rounded to 10 digits. **(F)**	[MATH] NUM ⟨round(⟩ 2-9

round(list,#decimals**)**	Returns list elements rounded to #decimals (≤9). **(F)**	MATH NUM ⟨round() 2-9
round(matrix**)**	Returns matrix elements rounded to 10 digits. **(F)**	MATH NUM ⟨round() 10-11
round(matrix,#decimals**)**	Returns matrix elements rounded to #decimals. **(F)**	MATH NUM ⟨round() 10-11
rowSwap(matrix,rowA, rowB**)**	Returns matrix with rowA of matrix swapped with rowB. **(F)**	MATRX MATH ⟨rowSwap() 10-14
row+(matrix,rowA,rowB**)**	Returns matrix with rowA of matrix added to rowB and stored in rowB. **(F)**	MATRX MATH ⟨row+() 10-14
***row(**value,matrix,row**)**	Returns matrix with row of matrix multiplied by value and stored in row. **(F)**	MATRX MATH ⟨*row() 10-14
***row+(**value,matrix, rowA,rowB**)**	Returns matrix with rowA of matrix multiplied by value, added to rowB, and stored in rowB. **(F)**	MATRX MATH ⟨*row+() 10-14
R▶Pr(X,Y**)**	Returns **R**, given rectangular coordinates X and Y. **(F)**	2nd [ANGLE] ⟨R▶Pr() 2-14
R▶Pθ**(**X,Y**)**	Returns θ, given rectangular coordinates X and Y. **(F)**	2nd [ANGLE] ⟨R▶Pθ() 2-14
Sci	Sets scientific display MODE. **(I)**	MODE ⟨Sci⟩ 1-10
Send(variable**)**	Sends contents of variable to external device. **(I)**	† PRGM I/O ⟨Send() 13-17
Seq	Sets MODE to graph sequences. **(I)**	† MODE ⟨Seq⟩ 1-11
seq(expression,variable, begin,end,increment**)**	Returns list created by evaluating expression for variable, from begin to end at increment. **(F)**	2nd [LIST] OPS ⟨seq() 11-8
Sequential	Sets MODE to graph sequentially. **(I)**	† MODE ⟨Sequential⟩ 1-11

Table of Functions and Instructions (Continued)

Shade(*lowerfunc,* ***upperfunc***)	Shade area above *lowerfunc* and below *upperfunc*. **(I)**	[2nd] [DRAW] DRAW ⟨Shade()⟩ 8-8
Shade(*lowerfunc,* ***upperfunc,resolution***)	Shade area above *lowerfunc,* below *upperfunc* with 1<*resolution*<9. **(I)**	[2nd] [DRAW] DRAW ⟨Shade()⟩ 8-8
Shade(*lowerfunc,* ***upperfunc,resolution,*** ***Xleft***)	Shade area above *lowerfunc,* below *upperfunc,* to right of **X**=*Xleft,* with 1<*resolution*<9. **(I)**	[2nd] [DRAW] DRAW ⟨Shade()⟩ 8-8
Shade(*lowerfunc,* ***upperfunc,resolution,*** ***Xleft,Xright***)	Shade area above *lowerfunc,* below *upperfunc,* to right of **X**=*Xleft,* to left of **X**=*Xright,* with 1<*resolution*<9. **(I)**	[2nd] [DRAW] DRAW ⟨Shade()⟩ 8-8
Simul	Sets simultaneous graphing MODE. **(I)**	† [MODE] ⟨Simul⟩ 1-11
sin *value*	Returns sine of *value*. **(F)**	[SIN] 2-3
sin *list*	Returns sine of *list* elements. **(F)**	[SIN] 2-3
sin⁻¹ *value*	Returns arcsine of *value*. **(F)**	[2nd] [sin⁻¹] 2-3
sin⁻¹ *list*	Returns arcsine of *list* elements. **(F)**	[2nd] [sin⁻¹] 2-3
sinh *value*	Returns hyperbolic sine of *value*. **(F)**	[MATH] HYP ⟨sinh⟩ 2-11
sinh *list*	Returns hyperbolic sine of *list* elements. **(F)**	[MATH] HYP ⟨sinh⟩ 2-11
sinh⁻¹ *value*	Returns hyperbolic arcsine of *value*. **(F)**	[MATH] HYP ⟨sinh⁻¹⟩ 2-11
sinh⁻¹ *list*	Returns hyperbolic arcsine of *list* elements. **(F)**	[MATH] HYP ⟨sinh⁻¹⟩ 2-11
solve(*expression,variable,* ***guess***)	Solves *expression* for *variable* using *guess* (a number or 2-element list), within bounds -1E99 and 1E99. **(F)**	[MATH] MATH ⟨solve()⟩ 2-8

solve(*expression,variable,* *guess,{lower,upper}*)	Solves *expression* for *variable* using *guess* (a number or 2-element list), between *lower* and *upper*. **(F)**	MATH MATH ⟨solve()⟩ 2-8
SortA(*listname*)	Sorts *listname* elements in ascending order. **(I)**	2nd [LIST] OPS ⟨SortA()⟩ 11-6
SortA(*listnameI,* *listnameD,listnameD,...*)	Sorts elements of *listnameI* in ascending order and *listnameD* as dependent lists. **(I)**	2nd [LIST] OPS ⟨SortA()⟩ 11-6
SortD(*listname*)	Sorts elements of *listname* in descending order. **(I)**	2nd [LIST] OPS ⟨SortD()⟩ 11-6
SortD(*listnameI,* *listnameD,listnameD,...*)	Sorts elements of *listnameI* in descending order and *listnameD* as dependent lists. **(I)**	2nd [LIST] OPS ⟨SortD()⟩ 11-6
Split	Sets split screen display MODE. **(I)**	† MODE ⟨Split⟩ 1-11
Square root: √*value*	Returns square root of *value*. **(F)**	2nd [√] 2-3
Square root: √*list*	Returns square root of *list* elements. **(F)**	2nd [√] 2-3
Squaring: *value*²	Returns *value* multiplied by itself. **(F)**	x^2 2-3
Squaring: *list*²	Returns *list* elements squared. **(F)**	x^2 2-3
Squaring: *matrix*²	Returns *matrix* multiplied by itself. **(F)**	x^2 10-11
Stop	Ends program execution, returns to Home screen. **(I)**	† PRGM CTL ⟨Stop⟩ 13-12
Store: *value*→*variable*	Stores *value* to *variable*. **(I)**	STO▶ 1-13
StoreGDB GDB*n*	Stores current graph as database **GDB***n*. **(I)**	2nd [DRAW] STO ⟨StoreGDB⟩ 8-15
StorePic Pic*n*	Stores current picture as picture **Pic***n*. **(I)**	2nd [DRAW] STO ⟨StorePic⟩ 8-14
Subtraction: *valueA*–*valueB*	Subtracts *valueB* from *valueA*. **(F)**	– 2-3
Subtraction: *value*–*list*	Subtracts *list* elements from *value*. **(F)**	– 2-3
Subtraction: *list*–*value*	Subtracts *value* from *list* elements. **(F)**	– 2-3

Table of Functions and Instructions (Continued)

Subtraction: *listA–listB*	Subtracts *listB* elements from *listA* elements. **(F)**	$\boxed{-}$	2-3
Subtraction: *matrixA–matrixB*	Subtracts *matrixB* elements from *matrixA* elements. **(F)**	$\boxed{-}$	10-10
sum *list*	Returns sum of elements of *list*. **(F)**	2nd [LIST] MATH ⟨sum⟩	11-10
tan *value*	Returns tangent of *value*. **(F)**	TAN	2-3
tan *list*	Returns tangent of *list* elements. **(F)**	TAN	2-3
tan⁻¹ *value*	Returns arctangent of *value*. **(F)**	2nd [tan⁻¹]	2-3
tan⁻¹ *list*	Returns arctangent of *list* elements. **(F)**	2nd [tan⁻¹]	2-3
Tangent(*expression,value***)**	Draws line tangent to *expression* at **X**=*value*. **(I)**	2nd [DRAW] DRAW ⟨Tangent(⟩	8-6
tanh *value*	Returns hyperbolic tangent of *value*. **(F)**	MATH HYP ⟨tanh⟩	2-11
tanh *list*	Returns hyperbolic tangent of *list* elements. **(F)**	MATH HYP ⟨tanh⟩	2-11
tanh⁻¹ *value*	Returns hyperbolic arctangent of *value*. **(F)**	MATH HYP ⟨tanh⁻¹⟩	2-11
tanh⁻¹ *list*	Returns hyperbolic arctangent of *list* elements. **(F)**	MATH HYP ⟨tanh⁻¹⟩	2-11
Text(*row,column,valueA,* *valueB . . .***)**	Writes value of *valueA* or "*text*" on graph beginning at pixel (*row,column*). 0≤*row*≤ 57, 0≤*column*≤94. **(I)**	2nd [DRAW] DRAW ⟨Text(⟩	8-10
Then *See* **If:Then**			
Time	Sets sequence graphs to plot over time. **(I)**	† WINDOW FORMAT ⟨Time⟩	6-5
Trace	Displays graph and enters TRACE mode. **(I)**	† TRACE	3-14
Transpose: *matrix*ᵀ	Returns *matrix* with elements transposed. **(F)**	MATRX MATH ⟨ᵀ⟩	10-12

2-Var Stats	Performs two-variable analysis using lists from SET UP CALCS menu. **(I)**	STAT CALC ⟨2-Var Stats⟩ 12-14
2-Var Stats *Xlist,Ylist*	Performs two-variable analysis using *Xlist* and *Ylist*. **(I)**	STAT CALC ⟨2-Var Stats⟩ 12-14
2-Var Stats *Xlist,Ylist,Flist*	Performs two-variable analysis using *Xlist* and *Ylist* with frequency *Flist*. **(I)**	STAT CALC ⟨2-Var Stats⟩ 12-14
Vertical *X*	Draws vertical line at *X*. **(I)**	2nd [DRAW] DRAW ⟨Vertical⟩ 8-5
Web	Sets sequence graphs to to trace as webs. **(I)**	† WINDOW FORMAT ⟨Web⟩ 6-5
While *condition* :*commands*:**End**	Executes *commands* while *condition* is true. **(I)**	† PRGM CTL ⟨While⟩ 13-9
valueA **xor** *valueB*	Returns 1 if only *valueA* or *valueB* = 0. **(F)**	2nd [TEST] LOGIC ⟨xor⟩ 2-16
ZBox	Displays graph to allow user to define new viewing WINDOW. **(I)**	ZOOM ZOOM ⟨ZBox⟩ 3-16
ZDecimal	Displays graph in new viewing WINDOW. **(I)**	ZOOM ZOOM ⟨ZDecimal⟩ 3-18
ZInteger	Displays graph in new viewing WINDOW. **(I)**	ZOOM ZOOM ⟨ZInteger⟩ 3-18
Zoom In	Displays graph in new viewing WINDOW. **(I)**	ZOOM ZOOM ⟨Zoom In⟩ 3-17
Zoom Out	Displays graph in new viewing WINDOW. **(I)**	ZOOM ZOOM ⟨Zoom Out⟩ 3-17
ZoomRcl	Displays graph in new viewing WINDOW. **(I)**	ZOOM ZOOM ⟨ZoomRcl⟩ 3-19
ZoomSto	Displays graph in new viewing WINDOW. **(I)**	ZOOM ZOOM ⟨ZoomSto⟩ 3-19
ZoomStat	Displays graph in new viewing WINDOW. **(I)**	ZOOM ZOOM ⟨ZoomStat⟩ 3-18
ZPrevious	Displays graph in new viewing WINDOW. **(I)**	ZOOM ZOOM ⟨ZPrevious⟩ 3-19
ZSquare	Displays graph in new viewing WINDOW. **(I)**	ZOOM ZOOM ⟨ZSquare⟩ 3-18
ZStandard	Displays graph in new viewing WINDOW. **(I)**	ZOOM ZOOM ⟨ZStandard⟩ 3-18
ZTrig	Displays graph in new viewing WINDOW. **(I)**	ZOOM ZOOM ⟨ZTrig⟩ 3-18

TI-82 Menu Map

Menus begin in the upper left of the keyboard. Default values are shown.

Y=

(**Func** MODE)	(**Par** MODE)	(**Pol** MODE)	(**Seq** MODE)
$Y_1=$	$X_{1T}=$	$r_1=$	$U_n=$
$Y_2=$	$Y_{1T}=$	$r_2=$	$V_n=$
$Y_3=$	$X_{2T}=$	$r_3=$	
$Y_4=$	$Y_{2T}=$	$r_4=$	
...	...	$r_5=$	
$Y_9=$	$X_{6T}=$	$r_6=$	
$Y_0=$	$Y_{6T}=$		

WINDOW

(**Func** MODE)	(**Par** MODE)	(**Pol** MODE)	(**Seq** MODE)
WINDOW	WINDOW	WINDOW	WINDOW
Xmin=-10	Tmin=0	θmin=0	UnStart=0
Xmax=10	Tmax=π*2	θmax=π*2	VnStart=0
Xscl=1	Tstep=π/24	θstep=π/24	nStart=0
Ymin=-10	Xmin=-10	Xmin=-10	nMin=0
Ymax=10	Xmax=10	Xmax=10	nMax=10
Yscl=1	Xscl=1	Xscl=1	Xmin=-10
	Ymin=-10	Ymin=-10	Xmax=10
	Ymax=10	Ymax=10	Xscl=1
	Yscl=1	Yscl=1	Ymin=-10
			Ymax=10
			Yscl=1

WINDOW

(**Func/Par/Pol** MODE)	(**Seq** MODE)
FORMAT	FORMAT
RectGC PolarGC	Time Web
CoordOn CoordOff	RectGC PolarGC
GridOff GridOn	CoordOn CoordOff
AxesOn AxesOff	GridOff GridOn
LabelOff LabelOn	AxesOn AxesOff
	LabelOff LabelOn

ZOOM   ZOOM

ZOOM	MEMORY	ZOOM FACTORS
1:ZBox	1:ZPrevious	XFact=4
2:Zoom In	2:ZoomSto	YFact=4
3:Zoom Out	3:ZoomRcl	
4:ZDecimal	4:SetFactors…	
5:ZSquare		
6:ZStandard		
7:ZTrig		
8:ZInteger		
9:ZoomStat		

2nd [CALC]

(**Func** MODE)	(**Par** MODE)	(**Pol** MODE)	(**Seq** MODE)
CALCULATE	CALCULATE	CALCULATE	(**Time** FORMAT)
1:value	1:value	1:value	CALCULATE
2:root	2:dy/dx	2:dy/dx	1:value
3:minimum	3:dy/dt	3:dr/dθ	
4:maximum	4:dx/dt		
5:intersect			
6:dy/dx			
7:∫f(x)dx			

2nd [TblSet]

TABLE SETUP
 TblMin=0
 ΔTbl=1
Indpnt: Auto Ask
Depend: Auto Ask

2nd [TblSet]

(PRGM editor)
TABLE SETUP
Indpnt: Auto Ask
Depend: Auto Ask

MODE

Normal Sci Eng
Float 0123456789
Radian Degree
Func Par Pol Seq
Connected Dot
Sequential Simul
FullScreen Split

2nd [STAT PLOT]

STAT PLOTS
1:Plot1…
  Off ⊯ L1 L2 □
2:Plot2…
  Off ⊯ L1 L2 □
3:Plot3…
  Off ⊯ L1 L2 □
4:PlotsOff
5:PlotsOn

2nd [STAT PLOT]

(PRGM editor)	(PRGM editor)	(PRGM editor)
PLOTS	TYPE	MARK
1:Plot1(	1:Scatter	1:□
2:Plot2(	2:xyLine	2:+
3:Plot3(	3:Boxplot	3:•
4:PlotsOff	4:Histogram	
5:PlotsOn		

STAT

EDIT	CALC
1:Edit…	1:1-Var Stats
2:SortA(	2:2-Var Stats
3:SortD(	3:SetUp…
4:ClrList	4:Med-Med
	5:LinReg(ax+b)
	6:QuadReg
	7:CubicReg
	8:QuartReg
	9:LinReg(a+bx)
	0:LnReg
	A:ExpReg
	B:PwrReg

STAT

(SetUp…)
1-Var Stats
Xlist: L1 L2 L3 L4 L5 L6
Freq:1 L1 L2 L3 L4 L5 L6
2-Var Stats
Xlist: L1 L2 L3 L4 L5 L6
Ylist: L1 L2 L3 L4 L5 L6
Freq:1 L1 L2 L3 L4 L5 L6

Menu Map (Continued)

[2nd] [LIST]

OPS	MATH
1:SortA(	1:min(
2:SortD(	2:max(
3:dim	3:mean(
4:Fill(	4:median(
5:seq(	5:sum
	6:prod

[MATH]

MATH	NUM	HYP	PRB
1:▶Frac	1:round(	1:sinh	1:rand
2:▶Dec	2:iPart	2:cosh	2:nPr
3:^{3}	3:fPart	3:tanh	3:nCr
4:$^3\sqrt{}$	4:int	4:sinh^{-1}	4:!
5:$^x\sqrt{}$	5:min(	5:cosh^{-1}	
6:fMin(	6:max(	6:tanh^{-1}	
7:fMax(			
8:nDeriv(			
9:fnInt(			
0:solve(			

[2nd] [TEST]

TEST	LOGIC
1:=	1:and
2:≠	2:or
3:>	3:xor
4:≥	4:not
5:<	
6:≤	

[MATRX]

NAMES	MATH	EDIT
1:[A] rxc	1:det	1:[A] rxc
2:[B] rxc	2:^{T}	2:[B] rxc
3:[C] rxc	3:dim	3:[C] rxc
4:[D] rxc	4:Fill(	4:[D] rxc
5:[E] rxc	5:identity	5:[E] rxc
	6:randM(	
	7:augment(	
	8:rowSwap(	
	9:row+(	
	0:*row(	
	A:*row+(	

[2nd] [ANGLE]

ANGLE
1:°
2:'
3:^{r}
4:▶DMS
5:R▶Pr(
6:R▶Pθ(
7:P▶Rx(
8:P▶Ry(

PRGM
```
┌──────────┬──────────┬──────────────┐
EXEC        EDIT        New
1:name      1:name      1:Create New
2:name      2:name
3:name      3:name
...         ...
```

PRGM
```
┌──────────────┬──────────────┬──────────────┐
(PRGM editor)   (PRGM editor)   (PRGM editor)
CTL             I/O             EXEC
1:If            1:Input         1:name
2:Then          2:Prompt        2:name
3:Else          3:Disp          3:name
4:For(          4:DispGraph     ...
5:While         5:DispTable
6:Repeat        6:Output(
7:End           7:getKey
8:Pause         8:ClrHome
9:Lbl           9:ClrTable
0:Goto          0:PrintScreen
A:IS>(          A:Get(
B:DS<(          B:Send(
C:Menu(
D:prgm
E:Return
F:Stop
```

2nd [DRAW]
```
┌──────────────┬──────────────┬──────────────┐
DRAW            POINTS          STO
1:ClrDraw       1:Pt-On(        1:StorePic
2:Line(         2:Pt-Off(       2:RecallPic
3:Horizontal    3:Pt-Change(    3:StoreGDB
4:Vertical      4:Pxl-On(       4:RecallGDB
5:Tangent(      5:Pxl-Off(
6:DrawF         6:Pxl-Change(
7:Shade(        7:pxl-Test(
8:DrawInv
9:Circle(
0:Text(
A:Pen
```

Menu Map (Continued)

`VARS`

VARS
1:Window…
2:Zoom…
3:GDB…
4:Picture…
5:Statistics…
6:Table…

`VARS`

(Window…) X/Y	(Window…) T/θ	(Window…) U/V	(Zoom…) ZX/ZY	(Zoom…) ZT/Zθ
1:Xmin	1:Tmin	1:UnStart	1:ZXmin	1:ZTmin
2:Xmax	2:Tmax	2:VnStart	2:ZXmax	2:ZTmax
3:Xscl	3:Tscl	3:nStart	3:ZXscl	3:ZTscl
4:Ymin	4:θmin	4:nMin	4:ZYmin	4:Zθmin
5:Ymax	5:θmax	5:nMax	5:ZYmax	5:Zθmax
6:Yscl	6:θstep		6:ZYscl	6:Zθstep
7:ΔX				
8:ΔY				
9:XFact				
0:YFact				

(Zoom…) ZU	(GDB…) GDB	(Picture…) PIC	(Statistics…) X/Y	(Statistics…) Σ
1:ZUnStart	1:GDB1	1:Pic1	1:n	1:Σx
2:ZVnStart	2:GDB2	2:Pic2	2:$\bar{x}$	2:Σx^2
3:ZnStart	3:GDB3	3:Pic3	3:Sx	3:Σy
4:ZnMin	4:GDB4	4:Pic4	4:σx	4:Σy^2
5:ZnMax	5:GDB5	5:Pic5	5:$\bar{y}$	5:Σxy
	6:GDB6	6:Pic6	6:Sy	
			7:σy	
			8:minX	
			9:maxX	
			0:minY	
			A:maxY	

(Statistics…) EQ	(Statistics…) BOX	(Statistics…) PTS	(Table…) TABLE
1:a	1:Q$_1$	1:x1	1:TblMin
2:b	2:Med	2:y1	2:ΔTbl
3:c	3:Q$_3$	3:x2	3:TblInput
4:d		4:y2	
5:e		5:x3	
6:r		6:y3	
7:RegEQ			

[2nd] [Y-VARS]

Y-Vars
1:Function…
2:Parametric…
3:Polar…
4:Sequence…
5:On/Off…

[2nd] [Y-VARS]

(Function…)	(Parametric…)	(Polar…)	(Sequence…)	(On/Off…)
FUNCTION	PARAMETRIC	$1:r_1=$	SEQUENCE	ON/OFF
$1:Y_1$	$1:X_{1T}$	$2:r_2=$	$1:U_n$	1:FnOn
$2:Y_2$	$2:Y_{1T}$	$3:r_3=$	$2:V_n$	2:FnOff
$3:Y_3$	$3:X_{2T}$	$4:r_4=$		
$4:Y_4$	$4:Y_{2T}$	$5:r_5=$		
…	…	$6:r_6=$		
$9:Y_9$	$A:X_{6T}$			
$0:Y_0$	$B:Y_{6T}$			

[2nd] [MEM]   [2nd] [MEM]

MEMORY	(Check RAM…)		(Delete…)	(Reset…)
1:Check RAM…	MEM FREE	28754	DELETE FROM…	RESET MEMORY
2:Delete…	Real	15	1:All…	1:No
3:Reset…	List	0	2:Real…	2:Reset
	Matrix	0	3:List…	
	Y-Vars	240	4:Matrix…	
	Prgm	14	5:Y-Vars…	
	Pic	0	6:Prgm…	
	GDB	0	7:Pic…	
			8:GDB…	

Table of Variables

The variables listed below are used by the TI-82 in various ways. Some have restrictions on their use.

User Variables

The variables **A** through **Z** and θ are defined as real numbers. You may store to them. However, the TI-82 can update **X**, **Y**, **R**, θ, and **T** during graphing, so you may wish to avoid using these variables for nongraphing activities.

The variables **L1** through **L6** are defined as lists. You cannot store another type of data to them.

The variables **[A]**, **[B]**, **[C]**, **[D]**, and, **[E]** are defined as matrices. You cannot store another type of data to them.

The variables **Pic1** through **Pic6** are pictures. You cannot store another type of data to them.

The variables **GDB1** through **GDB6** are graph databases. You cannot store another type of data to them.

You can store any string of characters, functions, instructions, or variable names to the functions Yn, Xn_T, rn, Un, and Vn directly or through the Y= editor. The validity of the string is determined when the function is evaluated.

System Variables

The variables below must be real numbers. You may store to them. The TI-82 can update some of them, as the result of a ZOOM, for example, so you may wish to avoid using these variables for nongraphing activities.

- **Xmin**, **Xmax**, **Xscl**, Δ**X**, **XFact**, **Tstep**, **UStart**, n**Min**, and other WINDOW variables.

- **ZXmin**, **ZXmax**, **ZXscl**, **ZTstep**, **ZUnStart**, **ZnMin**, and other ZOOM MEMORY variables.

The variables below are reserved for use by the TI-82. You cannot store to them.

- **n**, **x̄**, **minX**, **Σx**, **a**, **r**, **RegEQ**, **x1**, **y1**, and other statistical result variables.

- **Q1**, **Med**, **Q3**.

You can store to **Un-1** and **Vn-1** outside of graphing, but you cannot store to **n** outside of graphing.

Appendix B: Reference Information

This appendix provides supplemental information that may be helpful as you use the TI-82. It includes procedures that may help you correct problems with the calculator, and it describes the service and warranty provided by Texas Instruments.

Appendix Contents

Battery Information

The TI-82 uses two types of batteries: four AAA alkaline batteries and a lithium battery as a backup for retaining memory while you change the AAA batteries.

When to Replace the Batteries

As the batteries run down, the display begins to dim (especially during calculations), and you must adjust the contrast to a higher setting. If you find it necessary to set the contrast to a setting of 8 or 9, you will need to replace the batteries soon. You should change the lithium battery every three or four years.

Effects of Replacing the Batteries

If you do not remove both types of batteries at the same time or allow them to run down completely, you can change either type of battery without losing anything in memory.

Replacing the Batteries

1. Turn the calculator off and replace the slide cover over the keys to avoid inadvertently turning on the calculator. Turn the calculator so that the back is facing you.

2. Holding the calculator upright, push the latch on the battery cover down with your fingernail or a paper clip and pull the cover out.

3. Replace all four AAA alkaline batteries or the lithium battery. **To avoid loss of information stored in memory, the calculator must be off; do not remove the AAA batteries and the lithium battery at the same time.**

   • To replace the AAA alkaline batteries, remove all four discharged AAA batteries and install new ones as shown on the polarity diagram located in the battery compartment.

   • To replace the lithium battery, remove the screw and clip holding the lithium battery. Install the new battery, + side up. Then replace the screw and clip. Use a CR1616 or CR1620 (or equivalent) lithium battery.

   Dispose of used batteries properly. Do not incinerate or leave within reach of small children.

4. Replace the cover. When you turn the calculator on, the display shows the Home screen as it was when you last used it.

In Case of Difficulty

If you have difficulty operating the calculator, the following suggestions may help you to correct the problem.

Handling a Difficulty

1. If an error occurs, follow the procedure on page 1-22. Refer to the more detailed explanations about specific errors beginning on page B-6, if necessary.

2. If you cannot see anything on the display, follow the instructions on page 1-3 to adjust the contrast.

3. If the cursor is a checker-board pattern, memory is full. Press [2nd] [MEM] **Delete...** and delete some items from memory.

4. If the dotted bar busy indicator is displayed, a graph or program is paused and the TI-82 is waiting for input.

5. If the calculator does not appear to be working at all, be sure the batteries are installed properly and that they are fresh.

6. If the difficulty persists, see page B-10 for information on contacting Consumer Relations to discuss the problem or obtain service.

Accuracy Information

To maximize accuracy, the TI-82 carries more digits internally than it displays.

Computational Accuracy

Values in memory are stored using up to 14 digits with a 2-digit exponent.

- You can store a value in the WINDOW variables using up to 10 digits (12 digits for **Xscl**, **Yscl**, **Tstep**, and **θstep**).
- When a value is displayed, the displayed value is rounded as specified by the MODE setting (Chapter 1), with a maximum of 10 digits and a 2-digit exponent.
- **RegEQ** displays up to 14 digits.

Graphing Accuracy

Xmin is the center of the leftmost pixel, **Xmax** is the center of the next to the rightmost pixel. (The rightmost pixel is reserved for the busy indicator.) ΔX is the distance between the centers of two adjacent pixels.

- ΔX is calculated as (**Xmax–Xmin**)/**94**.
- If ΔX is entered from the Home screen or a program, then **Xmax** is calculated as **Xmin+ΔX∗94**.

Ymin is the center of the next to the bottom pixel, **Ymax** is the center of the top pixel. ΔY is the distance between the centers of two adjacent pixels.

- ΔY is calculated as (**Ymax-Ymin**)/**62**.
- If ΔY is entered from the Home screen or a program, then **Ymax** is calculated as **Ymin+ΔY∗62**.

Cursor coordinates are displayed as eight characters (which may include a negative sign, decimal point, and exponent). The values of **X** and **Y** are updated with a maximum of eight-digit accuracy.

root, **minimum**, **maximum**, and **intersect** on the CALCULATE menu are calculated with a tolerance of 1E-5; **∫f(x)dx** uses a tolerance of 1E-3. Therefore, the result displayed may not be accurate to all eight displayed digits. (In general, for most functions, there are at least 5 accurate digits.) The tolerance can be specified for the command-line functions **solve(**, **fMin(**, **fMax(**, and **fnInt(** on the MATH MATH menu.

Function Limits

Function	Range of Input Values
sin x, cos x, tan x	$0 \leq |x| < 10^{12}$ (radian or degree)
arcsin x, arccos x	$-1 \leq x \leq 1$
ln x, log x	$10^{-100} < x < 10^{100}$
e^x	$-10^{100} < x \leq 230.25850929940$
10^x	$-10^{100} < x < 100$
sinh x, cosh x	$|x| \leq 230.25850929940$
tanh x	$|x| < 10^{100}$
sinh^{-1} x	$|x| < 5 \times 10^{99}$
cosh^{-1} x	$1 \leq x < 5 \times 10^{99}$
tanh^{-1} x	$-1 < x < 1$
$\sqrt{x}$	$0 \leq x < 10^{100}$
$x!$	$0 \leq x \leq 69$, where x is an integer

Function Results

Function	Range of Result
sin^{-1} x, tan^{-1} x	-90° to 90° or -π/2 to π/2 (radians)
cos^{-1} x	0° to 180° or 0 to π (radians)

Error Conditions

When the TI-82 detects an error, it displays
ERR:*message* and the error menu. The general
procedure for correcting errors is described on page
1-22. Each error type, including possible causes and
suggestions for correction, are shown below.

ARGUMENT	A function or instruction does not have the correct number of arguments. See Appendix A and the appropriate chapter.
BAD GUESS	• For a CALC operation, Guess must be between Lower Bound and Upper Bound.
	• For the **solve(** function, *guess* must be between *lower* and *upper*.
	• The guess and several points around it are undefined.
	Examine a graph of the function. If the equation has a solution, change the bounds and/or the initial guess.
BOUND	• For a CALC operation , you must define Lower Bound < Upper Bound.
	• For **fMin(, fMax(, fnInt(,** and **solve(,** *lower* must be less than *upper*.
BREAK	You have pressed the [ON] key to break execution of a program, halt a DRAW instruction, or stop evaluaton of an expression.
DATA TYPE	You have entered a value or variable that is the wrong data type.
	• A function (including implied multiplication) or an instruction has an argument that is an invalid data type; for example, a list where a real number is required. See Appendix A and the appropriate chapter.
	• In an editor, you have entered a type that is not allowed; for example, a matrix as an element in the STAT list editor. See the appropriate chapter.
	• You are attempting to store to an incorrect data type; for example, a matrix to a list.
DIM MISMATCH	You are attempting to perform an operation that has more than one list or matrix, but the dimensions do not match.

DIVIDE BY 0	• You are attempting to divide by zero. This error does not occur during graphing. The TI-82 allows for undefined values on a graph.
	• You are attempting a linear regression with a vertical line.
DOMAIN	• The argument to a function or instruction is out of the valid range. See Appendix A and the appropriate chapter. This error does not occur during graphing. The TI-82 allows for undefined values on a graph.
	• You are attempting a logarithmic or power regression with a **-X** or an exponential regression with a **-Y**.
Duplicate Name	Unable to transmit item because a variable with that name already exists in receiving unit.
Error in Xmit	• Unable to transmit item. Check to see that the cable is firmly connected to both units and that the receiving unit is in Receive mode.
	• ON was used to break during transmission.
ILLEGAL NEST	You are attempting to use an invalid function in an argument to a function; for example, **seq(** within *expression* for **seq(**.
INCREMENT	• The increment in **seq(** is **0** or has the wrong sign. This error does not occur during graphing. The TI-82 allows for undefined values on a graph.
	• The increment for a loop is **0**.
INVALID	You are attempting to reference a variable or use a function in a place where it is not valid. For example, **Y**n cannot reference **Y**, **Xmin**, **ΔX** or **TblMin**.
INVALID DIM	• The dimension of the argument is not appropriate for the operation.
	• Matrix element dimensions and list element dimensions must be integers between 1 and 99.
	• A matrix must be square to invert it.
ITERATIONS	**solve(** has exceeded the maximum number of iterations permitted. Examine a graph of the function. If the equation has a solution, change the bounds and/or the initial guess.

Error Conditions (Continued)

LABEL	The label in the **Goto** instruction is not defined with a **Lbl** instruction in the program.
MEMORY	There is insufficient memory in which to perform the desired command. You must delete item(s) from memory (Chapter 15) before executing this command.
	Recursive problems, such as **A=A+2:A**, display this error.
	Interrupting an **If/Then**, **For**, **While**, or **Repeat** loop with a **Goto** that branches out of the loop can also cause this error, because the **End** statement that terminates the loop is never reached.
Memory Full	Unable to transmit item because there is insufficient available memory in the receiving unit. You may skip the item or exit Receive mode.
	During a memory backup, the receiving unit does not have enough memory to receive all items in memory in the sending unit. A message indicates the number of bytes the sending unit must delete to do the memory backup. Delete items and try again.
MODE	You are attempting to store to a WINDOW variable in another graphing MODE or to perform an instruction while in the wrong MODE, such as **DrawInv** in a graphing MODE other than **Func**.
OVERFLOW	You are attempting to enter, or have calculated, a number that is beyond the range of the calculator. This error does not occur during graphing. The TI-82 allows for undefined values on a graph.
RESERVED	You are attempting to use a system variable inappropriately. See Appendix A.
SIGN CHNG	The **solve(** function did not detect a sign change. Examine a graph of the function. If the equation has a solution, change the bounds and/or the initial guess.
SINGULAR MAT	• A singular matrix (determinate = 0) is not valid as the argument for $^{-1}$.
	• You are attempting a polynomial regression with lists that are not appropriate
	This error does not occur during graphing. The TI-82 allows for undefined values on a graph.

SINGULARITY	*expression* in the **solve(** function contains a singularity (a point at which the function is not defined). Examine a graph of the function. If the equation has a solution, change the bounds and/or the initial guess.
STAT	You are attempting a stat calculation with lists that are not appropriate. • Statistical analyses must have at least two data points. • **Med-Med** must have at least three points in each partition. • Freq, when used, must be an integer $\geq$ **0**. • **(Xmax-Xmin)/Xscl** must be $\leq$ 47 for a histogram.
STAT PLOT	You are trying to display a graph when there is a StatPlot On that uses an undefined list.
SYNTAX	The command contains a syntax error. Look for misplaced functions, arguments, parentheses, or commas. See Appendix A and the appropriate chapter.
TOL NOT MET	The algorithm cannot return a result accurate to the requested tolerance.
UNDEFINED	You are referencing a variable that is not currently defined; for example, a stat variable when there is no current calculation because a list has been edited or when the variable is not valid for the current calculation, such as a after **Med-Med**.
WINDOW RANGE	There is a problem with the WINDOW variables. • You may have defined **Xmax**$\leq$**Xmin**, **Ymax**$\leq$**Ymin**, θ**max**$\leq\theta$**min** and θ**step>0** (or vice versa), **Tstep=0**, or **Tmax**$\leq$**Tmin** and **Tstep>0** (or vice versa). • WINDOW variables are too small or too large to graph correctly, which can occur if you attempt to zoom in or out so far that you are not within the numerical range of the calculator.
ZOOM	A point or a line, rather than a box, is defined in **ZBox** or a math error resulted from a ZOOM operation.

Service Information

If the solutions suggested by "In Case of Difficulty" do not correct a problem you may have with your TI-82, you may call or write Texas Instruments Consumer Relations.

For Service and General Information

If you have questions about service or about the general use of the TI-82, call Consumer Relations toll-free at:

1-800-TI-CARES (1-800-842-2737)

You may also write to:

**Consumer Relations
Texas Instruments Incorporated
P.O. Box 53
Lubbock, Texas 79408-0053**

Please contact Consumer Relations:

* Before returning the product for service.
* For information on our express service option for fast return delivery.
* For general information about using the TI-82.
* For information about purchasing related products.

For Technical Information

If you have technical questions about the TI-82 or programming applications, you may call the Technical Support Group of Consumer Relations at:

1-806-741-2663

Please note that this is a toll number, and collect calls are not accepted.

You may also write to:

**Technical Support Group, Consumer Relations
Texas Instruments Incorporated
P.O. Box 53
Lubbock, Texas 79408-0053**

Returning Your Calculator for Service

A defective calculator will be either repaired or replaced with the same or comparable reconditioned model (at TI's option) when it is returned, postage prepaid, to a Texas Instruments Service Facility.

Texas Instruments cannot assume responsibility for loss or damage during incoming shipment. For your protection, carefully package the calculator for shipment and insure it with the carrier. Be sure to enclose the following items with your calculator:

• Your full return address and daytime phone number

• Any accessories related to the problem

• A note describing the problem you experienced

• A copy of your sales receipt or other proof of purchase to determine warranty status

Please ship the calculator postage prepaid; COD shipments cannot be accepted.

In-Warranty Service

For a calculator covered under the warranty period, no charge is made for service.

Out-of-Warranty Service

A flat-rate charge by model is made for out-of-warranty service. To obtain the service charge for a particular model, contact Consumer Relations before returning the product for service. (We cannot hold products in the Service Facility while providing charge information.)

Texas Instruments Service Facilities

**U.S. Residents
(U.S. Postal Service)**
Texas Instruments
P.O. Box 2500
Lubbock, Texas 79408

**U.S. Residents
(other carriers)**
Texas Instruments
2305 N. University
Lubbock, Texas 79408

Canadian Residents Only
Texas Instruments
41 Shelley Road
Richmond Hill, Ontario L4C 5G4

One-Year Limited Warranty

This Texas Instruments electronic calculator warranty extends to the original consumer purchaser of the product.

Warranty Duration

This calculator is warranted to the original consumer purchaser for a period of one (1) year from the original purchase date.

Warranty Coverage

This calculator is warranted against defective materials or workmanship. **This warranty is void if the product has been damaged by accident, unreasonable use, neglect, improper service, or other causes not arising out of defects in material or workmanship.**

Warranty Disclaimers

Any implied warranties arising out of this sale, including but not limited to the implied warranties of merchantability and fitness for a particular purpose, are limited in duration to the above one-year period. Texas Instruments shall not be liable for loss of use of the calculator or other incidental or consequential costs, expenses, or damages incurred by the consumer or any other user.

Some states do not allow the exclusion or limitations of implied warranties or consequential damages, so the above limitations or exclusions may not apply to you.

Legal Remedies

This warranty gives you specific legal rights, and you may also have other rights that vary from state to state.

Warranty Performance

During the above one-year warranty period, a defective TI calculator will either be repaired or replaced with a reconditioned comparable model (at TI's option) when the product is returned, postage prepaid, to a Texas Instruments Service Facility.

The repaired or replacement calculator will be in warranty for the remainder of the original warranty period or for six months, whichever is longer. Other than the postage requirement, no charge will be made for such repair or replacement.

Texas Instruments strongly recommends that you insure the product for value prior to mailing.

Index

- T -

^{T} (transpose), 10-12, A-20
T variable, 4-5, 4-6, 7-3, A-28
Tables, GS-7 to GS-9, 7-1 to 7-6
TABLE SETUP screen, 7-2, 7-3, 9-3
Table variables, 1-19
tan, tan⁻¹, 2-3, A-20, B-5
Tangent(, 8-3, 8-6, A-20
Tangent line, 8-6
tanh, tanh⁻¹, 2-11, A-20, B-5
TblMin, 1-19, 7-2, 7-3, 7-5, 12-4, 12-5
TEST menu, 2-15
TEST LOGIC menu, 2-16
Text(, 8-3, 8-10, 9-4, A-20
Then, 13-7, 13-8, A-20
θ variable, 4-6, 5-5, 5-6, 7-3, A-28
θmax, θmin, 5-4, 5-5, 5-6, B-4, B-9
θstep, 5-4, 5-5, 5-6, B-4, B-9
Time FORMAT, 6-4 to 6-6, A-20
Tmax, Tmin, 4-4, 4-5, B-4, B-9
TOL NOT MET error, B-9
Tolerance, 2-6, 2-7, 3-23, 3-24
Trace, 3-15, A-20
TRACE, GS-11, 3-14, 3-15, 4-6, 5-6, 6-5, 9-3, 12-21
Transmitting, 16-1 to 16-8
Transpose: ^{T}, 10-12, A-20
Trig functions, 2-3
Tstep, 4-4, 4-5, B-4, B-9
Turning functions on and off, 1-19
Turning the TI-82 on and off, 1-2
2-Var Stats, 12-13, 12-14, A-21
Two-variable statistics, 12-13, 12-14

- U -

U*n*, U*n-1*, 1-19, 6-2 to 6-6, 11-8, A-28
UNDEFINED error, B-9
U*n*Start, 6-4, 6-6, A-28
Upper bound, 2-8, 3-23, B-6

- V -

value, 3-21, 4-6, 5-6
Variables, x, 1-12, 1-13, A-28
VARS menu, 1-19, 3-9
Vertical, 8-3, 8-5, A-21
Vertical line, 8-5
Viewing rectangle, viewing window.
   See WINDOW
V*n*, V*n-1*, 1-19, 6-2 to 6-6, 11-8, A-28
V*n*Start, 6-6, A-28

- W -

WARNING Memory Backup message, 16-8
Warranty information, B-12
Web FORMAT, 6-5, 6-6, A-21
While, 13-7, 13-9, A-21, B-8
WINDOW, GS-10, 1-19, 3-8 to 3-9, 3-16 to 3-20, 4-3 to 4-6, 5-4 to 5-6, 6-4 to 6-6, 12-21, 13-15, A-28, B-8
WINDOW FORMAT, 3-10, 9-3
WINDOW RANGE error, B-9

- X -

X,T,θ key, 3-5, 4-3, 5-3
X, 3-5, 4-5, 4-6, 5-5, 5-6, 6-5, 6-6, 7-3, A-28, B-4
$\bar{x}$, 12-14, A-28
x1, x2, x3, 12-14, 12-15, A-28
X*n*T functions, 1-19, 4-3, A-28
XFact variable, 3-17, 3-19, 3-20
Xlist, 12-20
Xmax, Xmin, Xscl, 3-8, 3-13, 3-18, 4-4, 4-6, 5-4, 5-6, 6-4, 6-6, 12-19, 13-15, A-28, B-4, B-9
xor, 2-16, A-21
X/Y (VARS) menu, 1-19, 12-14
xyLine, 12-18, 12-20 to 12-22

Notes

Notes

Notes

Notes

Notes

Notes

Notes

Notes

Notes

Notes